# AUTHORS

ELAINE MEI AOKI
VIRGINIA A. ARNOLD
JAMES FLOOD
JAMES V. HOFFMAN
DIANE LAPP
MIRIAM MARTINEZ

ANNEMARIE SULLIVAN
 PALINCSAR
MICHAEL PRIESTLEY
NANCY ROSER
CARL B. SMITH

WILLIAM H. TEALE
JOSEFINA VILLAMIL
 TINAJERO
ARNOLD W. WEBB
PEGGY E. WILLIAMS
KAREN D. WOOD

## MACMILLAN/McGRAW-HILL SCHOOL PUBLISHING COMPANY

NEW YORK    CHICAGO    COLUMBUS

# AUTHORS, CONSULTANTS, AND REVIEWERS

## WRITE IDEA! Authors

Elaine Mei Aoki, James Flood, James V. Hoffman, Diane Lapp, Ana Huerta Macias, Miriam Martinez, Ann McCallum, Michael Priestley, Nancy Roser, Carl B. Smith, William Strong, William H. Teale, Charles Temple, Josefina Villamil Tinajero, Arnold W. Webb, Peggy E. Williams

The approach to writing in Macmillan/McGraw-Hill Reading/Language Arts is based on the strategies and approaches to composition and conventions of language in Macmillan/McGraw-Hill's writing-centered language arts program, WRITE IDEA!

## Multicultural and Educational Consultants

Alma Flor Ada, Yvonne Beamer, Joyce Buckner, Helen Gillotte, Cheryl Hudson, Narcita Medina, Lorraine Monroe, James R. Murphy, Sylvia Peña, Joseph B. Rubin, Ramon Santiago, Cliff Trafzer, Hai Tran, Esther Lee Yao

## Literature Consultants

Ashley Bryan, Joan I. Glazer, Paul Janeczko, Margaret H. Lippert

## International Consultants

Edward B. Adams, Barbara Johnson, Raymond L. Marshall

## Music and Audio Consultants

John Farrell, Marilyn C. Davidson, Vincent Lawrence, Sarah Pirtle, Susan R. Snyder, Rick and Deborah Witkowski

## Teacher Reviewers

Terry Baker, Jane Bauer, James Bedi, Nora Bickel, Vernell Bowen, Donald Cason, Jean Chaney, Carolyn Clark, Alan Cox, Kathryn DesCarpentrie, Carol L. Ellis, Roberta Gale, Brenda Huffman, Erma Inscore, Sharon Kidwell, Elizabeth Love, Isabel Marcus, Elaine McCraney, Michelle Moraros, Earlene Parr, Dr. Richard Potts, Jeanette Pulliam, Michael Rubin, Henrietta Sakamaki, Kathleen Cultron Sanders, Belinda Snow, Dr. Jayne Steubing, Margaret Mary Sulentic, Barbara Tate, Seretta Vincent, Willard Waite, Barbara Wilson, Veronica York

# ACKNOWLEDGMENTS

*The publisher gratefully acknowledges permission to reprint the following copyrighted material:*

"And my heart soars" by Chief Dan George. Copyright © 1974 by Chief Dan George and Helmut Hirnschall. Reprinted by permission of Hancock House Publishing Ltd. 19313 Zeroz Ave., Surrey, BC V3S 5J9, Canada.

Illustration from BEAT THE STORY DRUM, PUM-PUM retold and illustrated by Ashley Bryan. Copyright © 1980 Ashley Bryan. Reprinted with permission of Atheneum Publishers, an imprint of Macmillan Publishing Company.

"Bringing the Rain to Kapiti Plain" is from BRINGING THE RAIN TO KAPITI PLAIN by Verna Aardema, illustrated by Beatriz Vidal. Text copyright © 1981 by Verna Aardema. Illustrations copyright © 1981 by Beatriz Vidal. Used by permission of Dial Books for Young Readers, a division of Penguin Books USA Inc.

"Cloudy With a Chance of Meatballs" is from CLOUDY WITH A CHANCE OF MEATBALLS by Judi Barrett. Copyright © 1978 by Judi Barrett, illustrations copyright © 1978 by Ron Barrett. Reprinted with permission from Atheneum Publishers, an imprint of Macmillan Publishing Company.

Illustration from THE DANCING GRANNY retold and illustrated by Ashley Bryan. Copyright © 1977 by Ashley Bryan. Reprinted with permission of Atheneum Publishers, an imprint of Macmillan Publishing Company.

"Dream Wolf" is from DREAM WOLF by Paul Goble. Copyright © 1990 by Paul Goble. Reprinted by permission from Bradbury Press, an affiliate of Macmillan, Inc.

Jacket cover: THE GIRL WHO LOVED WILD HORSES by Paul Goble. Copyright 1978 by Paul Goble. Reprinted with the permission of Bradbury Press, an affiliate of Macmillan, Inc.

"Gone" from ONE AT A TIME by David McCord. Copyright © 1970 by David McCord. By permission of Little, Brown and Company.

"The Great Kapok Tree" is from THE GREAT KAPOK TREE by Lynne Cherry. Copyright © 1990 by Lynne Cherry. Reprinted by permission of Harcourt Brace Jovanovich, Inc.

"In Memory" by Ericka Northrop from *JACK AND JILL*. Copyright © 1989 by Children's Better Health Institute, Benjamin Franklin Literary & Medical Society. Indianapolis, Indiana. Used by permission.

"In Time of Silver Rain" from SELECTED POEMS by Langston Hughes. Copyright © 1938 and renewed 1966 by Langston Hughes. Reprinted by permission of Alfred A. Knopf Inc.

Jacket cover: ISLAND BOY by Barbara Cooney. Copyright © 1988 by Barbara Cooney Porter. Used by permission of Viking Penguin, a division of Penguin Books USA Inc.

Illustration from LION AND THE OSTRICH CHICKS retold and illustrated by Ashley Bryan. Copyright © 1986 Ashley Bryan. Reprinted with permission of Atheneum Publishers, an imprint of Macmillan Publishing Company.

"Miss Rumphius" is from MISS RUMPHIUS by Barbara Cooney. Copyright © 1982 by Barbara Cooney Porter. Used by permission of Viking Penguin, a division of Penguin Books USA, Inc.

"Operation Rescue: Saving Sea Life From Oil Spills" is from the September 1990 issue of *3-2-1 CONTACT Magazine*. Copyright © 1990 Children's Television Workshop (New York, New York). All rights reserved. Used by permission.

*(continued on page 327)*

To the book designers who conducted a visual symphony of talent to bring this literary experience to you.

Paula Darmofal
Beth Beauvais Walberg

To you, the readers, from all the designers and artists who still feel the joy and magic of reading and strove to pass those feelings on.

Ilse Bergins
Johanna Madia

# It's Up To Us

## The Streets Are Free

A story
*by Kurusa*
*illustrated by Sandra Speidel*

The streets are free for anyone to use—but they don't make good playgrounds. The children of San José join together to try to solve their problem—a place to play. This story is based on events that took place in Caracas, Venezuela.

# WEATHER THE STORM

# To The Rescue!

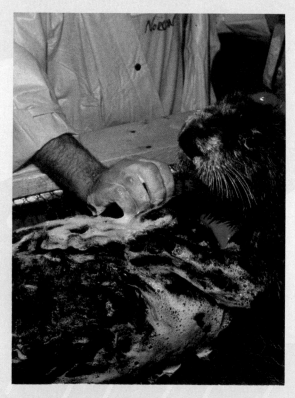

# CONTENTS

# IT'S UP TO US

Every living thing—you, me,
the cat, the sparrow, trees,
butterflies—all of us need good
air and pure water and enough
food. The earth gives us air
and food and water. It keeps
us alive. Let's return the favor.

MARGARET GABEL
from *Sparrows Don't Drop Candy Wrappers*

# Miss Rumphius

The Lupine Lady lives in a small house overlooking the sea. In between the rocks around her house grow blue and purple and rose-colored flowers. The Lupine Lady is little and old. But she has not always been that way. I know. She is my great-aunt, and she told me so.

Once upon a time she was a little girl named Alice, who lived in a city by the sea. From the front stoop she could see the wharves and the bristling masts of tall ships. Many years ago her grandfather had come to America on a large sailing ship.

Story and Pictures by Barbara Cooney

Now he worked in the shop at the bottom of the house, making figureheads for the prows of ships, and carving Indians out of wood to put in front of cigar stores. For Alice's grandfather was an artist. He painted pictures, too, of sailing ships and places across the sea. When he was very busy, Alice helped him put in the skies.

In the evening Alice sat on her grandfather's knee and listened to his stories of faraway places. When he had finished, Alice would say, "When I grow up, I too will go to faraway places, and when I grow old, I too will live beside the sea."

"That is all very well, little Alice," said her grandfather, "but there is a third thing you must do."

"What is that?" asked Alice.

"You must do something to make the world more beautiful," said her grandfather.

"All right," said Alice. But she did not know what that could be.

In the meantime Alice got up and washed her face and ate porridge for breakfast. She went to school and came home and did her homework.

And pretty soon she was grown up.

Then my Great-aunt Alice set out to do the three things she had told her grandfather she was going to do. She left home and went to live in another city far from the sea and the salt air. There she worked in a library, dusting books and keeping them from getting mixed up, and helping people find the ones they wanted. Some of the books told her about faraway places.

People called her Miss Rumphius now.

Sometimes she went to the conservatory in the middle of the park. When she stepped inside on a wintry day, the warm moist air wrapped itself around her, and the sweet smell of jasmine filled her nose.

"This is almost like a tropical isle," said Miss Rumphius. "But not quite."

So Miss Rumphius went to a real tropical island, where people kept cockatoos and monkeys as pets. She walked on long beaches, picking up beautiful shells. One day she met the Bapa Raja, king of a fishing village.

"You must be tired," he said. "Come into my house and rest."

So Miss Rumphius went in and met the Bapa Raja's wife. The Bapa Raja himself fetched a green coconut and cut a slice off the top so that Miss Rumphius could drink the coconut water inside. Before she left, the Bapa Raja gave her a beautiful mother-of-pearl shell on which he had painted a bird of paradise and the words, "You will always remain in my heart."

"You will always remain in mine too," said Miss Rumphius.

My great-aunt Miss Alice Rumphius
climbed tall mountains where the snow
never melted. She went through jungles
and across deserts. She saw lions
playing and kangaroos jumping. And
everywhere she made friends she would
never forget. Finally she came to the
Land of the Lotus-Eaters, and there,
getting off a camel, she hurt her back.

"What a foolish thing to do," said
Miss Rumphius. "Well, I have certainly
seen faraway places. Maybe it is time to
find my place by the sea."

And it was, and she did.

From the porch of her new house
Miss Rumphius watched the sun come
up; she watched it cross the heavens
and sparkle on the water; and she saw
it set in glory in the evening. She
started a little garden among the rocks
that surrounded her house, and she
planted a few flower seeds in the
stony ground. Miss Rumphius was
*almost* perfectly happy.

"But there is still one more thing
I have to do," she said. "I have to do
something to make the world more
beautiful."

But what? "The world already is
pretty nice," she thought, looking out
over the ocean.

The next spring Miss Rumphius was not very well. Her back was bothering her again, and she had to stay in bed most of the time.

.The flowers she had planted the summer before had come up and bloomed in spite of the stony ground. She could see them from her bedroom window, blue and purple and rose-colored.

"Lupines," said Miss Rumphius with satisfaction. "I have always loved lupines the best. I wish I could plant more seeds this summer so that I could have still more flowers next year."

But she was not able to.

After a hard winter spring came. Miss Rumphius was feeling much better. Now she could take walks again. One afternoon she started to go up and over the hill, where she had not been in a long time.

"I don't believe my eyes!" she cried when she got to the top. For there on the other side of the hill was

a large patch of blue and purple and rose-colored lupines!

"It was the wind," she said as she knelt in delight. "It was the wind that brought the seeds from my garden here! And the birds must have helped!"

Then Miss Rumphius had a wonderful idea!

She hurried home and got out her seed catalogues. She sent off to the very best seed house for five bushels of lupine seed.

All that summer Miss Rumphius, her pockets full of seeds, wandered over fields and headlands, sowing lupines. She scattered seeds along the highways and down the country lanes. She flung handfuls of them around the schoolhouse and back of the church. She tossed them into hollows and along stone walls.

Her back didn't hurt her any more at all.

Now some people called her That Crazy Old Lady.

The next spring there were lupines everywhere. Fields and hillsides were covered with blue and purple and rose-colored flowers. They bloomed along the highways and down the lanes. Bright patches lay around the schoolhouse and back of the

24

church. Down in the hollows and along the stone walls grew the beautiful flowers.

Miss Rumphius had done the third, the most difficult thing of all!

My Great-aunt Alice, Miss Rumphius, is very old now. Her hair is very white. Every year there are more and more lupines. Now they call her the Lupine Lady. Sometimes my friends stand with me outside her gate, curious to see the old, old lady who planted the fields of lupines. When she invites us in, they come slowly. They think she is the oldest woman in the world. Often she tells us stories of faraway places.

"When I grow up," I tell her, "I too will go to faraway places and come home to live by the sea."

"That is all very well, little Alice," says my aunt, "but there is a third thing you must do."

"What is that?" I ask.

"You must do something to make the world more beautiful."

"All right," I say.

But I do not know yet
what that can be.

# Meet Barbara Cooney

There really was a woman in Maine who collected lupine seeds and "flung handfuls of them around," just as in *Miss Rumphius*. The woman wasn't exactly like the character in the book, but she provided "the seed of the idea" for Barbara Cooney. The author helped the idea grow until she had a story that was like a modern fairy tale.

People often ask Barbara Cooney how she came to write or illustrate her books. This is what she said when asked about her drawings in *Chanticleer and the Fox:* "That question is a little embarrassing because the answer is so simple. I just happened to want to draw chickens." (Her "chicken" book received the Caldecott Medal.)

Barbara Cooney's illustrations always contain many wonderful details, all of which are accurate. "If I put enough in my pictures," she says, "there will be something for everyone." She received a second Caldecott Medal for *Ox-Cart Man*, and a story she both wrote and illustrated, *Island Boy*, was a Boston Globe/Horn Book Honor Book.

# From Sea to

From California and the Pacific Ocean to New York and the Atlantic Ocean, people are saying it really is up to us!

## Oakland, California

Students from the Glenview and La Escuelita schools created four murals of their city. But they left one thing out—litter! Why? They wanted people to see Oakland as a beautiful, litter-free place to live.

As one student, Nathaniel Gallardo, explained, "I hope that when people see our murals, they will think that these kids know how beautiful Oakland is because of the way they painted it."

# Shining Sea

MR. VELEZ
6th GRADE

BOAT HOUSE

FAIRYLAND

Courtesy of Festival at the Lake, Oakland, California.

### New York, New York

In the middle of a New York City neighborhood, old tires, rusty bedsprings, and abandoned cars once covered three lots. Then the "Lot Busters" arrived. This group of neighborhood adults and children "found" a secret garden under all the junk.

The "Lot Busters" spent six months hauling away trash and preparing the lots for planting. People didn't mind the hard work, though. As Elena Maldonado said, "When you work with family and friends, even pushing a two-ton car out of a lot can be fun."

31

# In Memory

It took a wise man to dream big,
To dream great,
To talk of peace, brotherhood, and love
When all around was hate.
It took a strong man
To stand tall,
To speak of liberty and justice
And dignity for all.
He saw a great country
With some growing still to do.
He dreamed of a better world
Where freedom could ring true.
And so today we'll gather
For a birthday celebration
For a man who sought to change the mind
And heart of a nation.
Of liberty and brotherhood and peace
Today we'll sing
As we celebrate the memory of
Martin Luther King.

*Ericka Northrop*

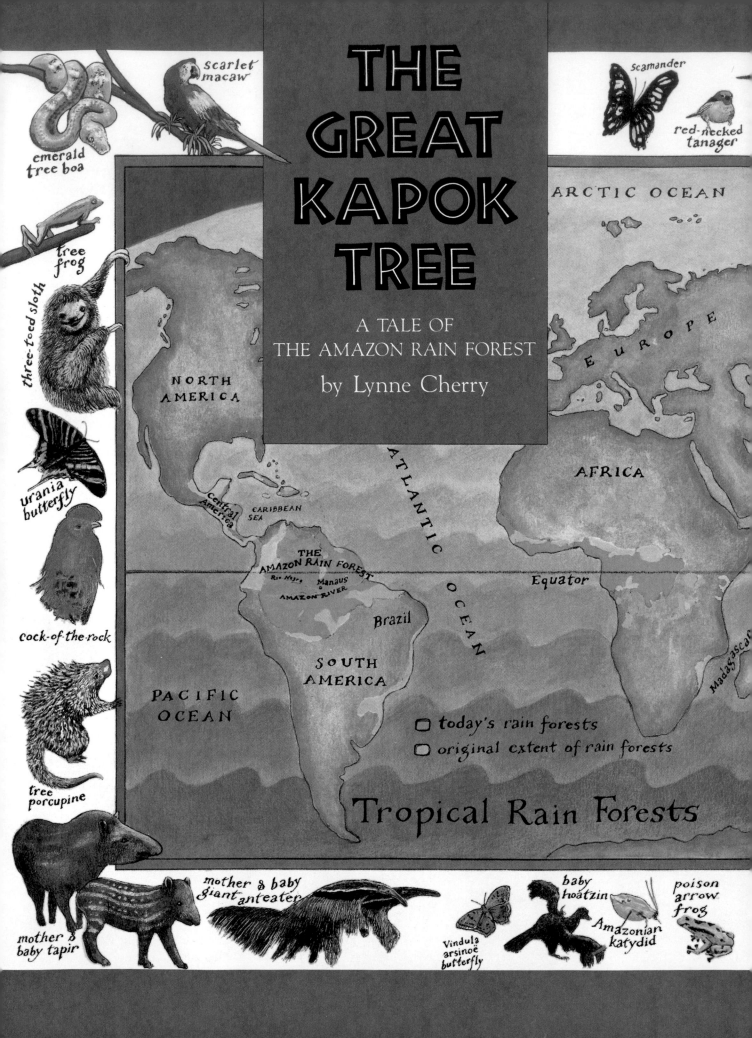

emerald
tree boa

scarlet
macaw

scamander

red-necked
tanager

# THE GREAT KAPOK TREE

## A TALE OF
## THE AMAZON RAIN FOREST

### by Lynne Cherry

tree
frog

three-toed sloth

ARCTIC OCEAN

NORTH
AMERICA

EUROPE

AFRICA

Central
America

CARIBBEAN
SEA

ATLANTIC

OCEAN

Equator

urania
butterfly

THE
AMAZON RAIN FOREST

Rio Negro    Manaus

AMAZON RIVER

Brazil

Madagascar

cock-of-the-rock

SOUTH
AMERICA

PACIFIC
OCEAN

☐ today's rain forests
☐ original extent of rain forests

tree
porcupine

# Tropical Rain Forests

mother & baby
giant anteater

baby
hoatzin

poison
arrow
frog

mother &
baby tapir

Vindula
arsinoë
butterfly

Amazonian
katydid

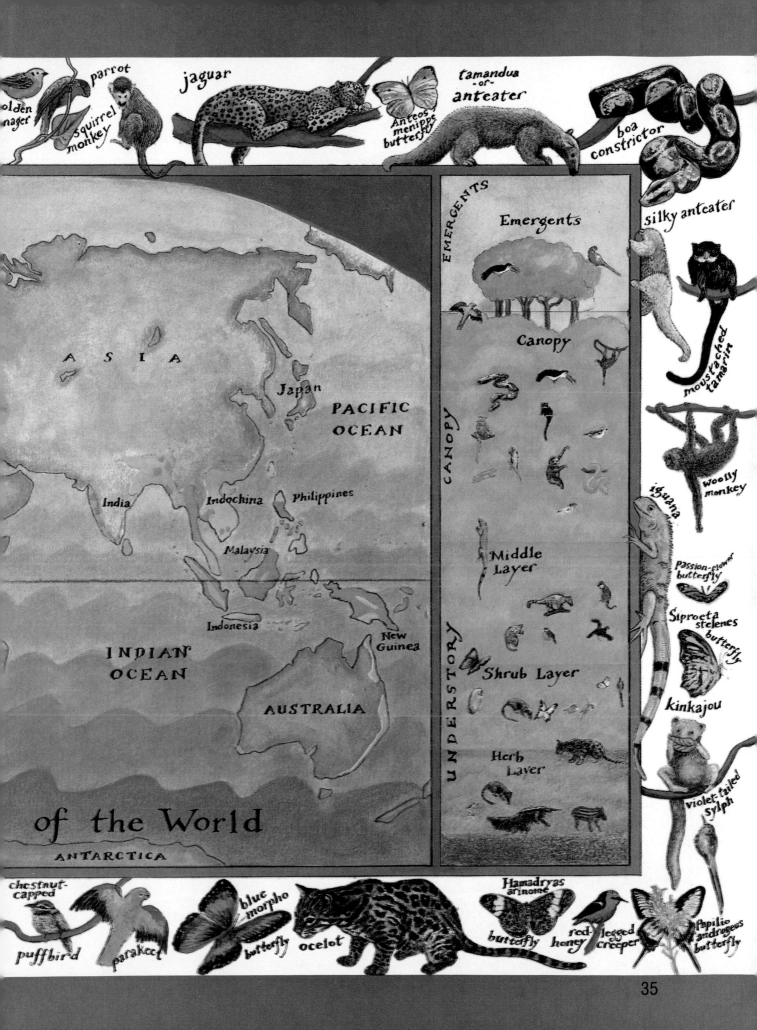

parrot

golden nager

squirrel monkey

jaguar

Anteos menippe butterfly

tamandua -or- anteater

boa constrictor

silky anteater

moustached tamarin

ASIA

Japan

PACIFIC OCEAN

India

Indochina

Philippines

Malaysia

Indonesia

New Guinea

INDIAN OCEAN

AUSTRALIA

of the World

ANTARCTICA

EMERGENTS

Emergents

Canopy

CANOPY

Middle Layer

Shrub Layer

UNDERSTORY

Herb Layer

woolly monkey

iguana

passion-flower butterfly

Siproeta stelenes butterfly

kinkajou

violet-tailed sylph

chestnut-capped puffbird

parakeet

blue morpho butterfly

ocelot

Hamadryas arinome butterfly

red-legged honey creeper

Papilio androgeus butterfly

*I*n the Amazon rain forest it is always hot, and in that heat everything grows, and grows, and grows. The tops of the trees in the rain forest are called the canopy. The canopy is a sunny place that touches the sky. The animals that live there like lots of light. Colorful parrots fly from tree to tree. Monkeys leap from branch to branch. The bottom of the rain forest is called the understory. The animals that live in the understory like darkness. There, silent snakes curl around hanging vines. Graceful jaguars watch and wait.

And in this steamy environment the great Kapok tree shoots up through the forest and emerges above the canopy.

This is the story of a community of animals that live in one such tree in the rain forest.

Two men walked into the rain forest. Moments before, the forest had been alive with the sounds of squawking birds and howling monkeys. Now all was quiet as the creatures watched the two men and wondered why they had come.

The larger man stopped and pointed to a great Kapok tree. Then he left.

The smaller man took the ax he carried and struck the trunk of the tree. Whack! Whack! Whack! The sounds of the blows rang through the forest. The wood of the tree was very hard. Chop! Chop! Chop! The man wiped off the sweat that ran down his face and neck. Whack! Chop! Whack! Chop!

Soon the man grew tired. He sat down to rest at the foot of the great Kapok tree. Before he knew it, the heat and hum of the forest had lulled him to sleep.

A boa constrictor lived in the Kapok tree. He slithered down its trunk to where the man was sleeping. He looked at the gash the ax had made in the tree. Then the huge snake slid very close to the man and hissed in his ear: "Senhor, this tree is a tree of miracles. It is my home, where generations of my ancestors have lived. Do not chop it down."

A bee buzzed in the sleeping man's ear: "Senhor, my hive is in this Kapok tree, and I fly from tree to tree and flower to flower collecting pollen. In this way I pollinate the trees and flowers throughout the rain forest. You see, all living things depend on one another."

A troupe of monkeys scampered down from the canopy of the Kapok tree. They chattered to the sleeping man: "Senhor, we have seen the ways of man. You chop down one tree, then come back for another and another. The roots of these great trees will wither and die, and there will be nothing left to hold the earth in place. When the heavy rains come, the soil will be washed away and the forest will become a desert."

A toucan, a macaw, and a cock-of-the-rock flew down from the canopy. "Senhor!" squawked the toucan, "you must not cut down this tree. We have flown over the rain forest and seen what happens once you begin to chop down the trees. Many people settle on the land. They set fires to clear the underbrush, and soon the forest disappears. Where once there was life and beauty only black and smoldering ruins remain."

A bright and small tree frog crawled along the edge of a leaf. In a squeaky voice he piped in the man's ear: "Senhor, a ruined rain forest means ruined lives . . . many ruined lives. You will leave many of us homeless if you chop down this great Kapok tree."

45

A jaguar had been sleeping along a branch in the middle of the tree. Because his spotted coat blended into the dappled light and shadows of the understory, no one had noticed him. Now he leapt down and padded silently over to the sleeping man. He growled in his ear: "Senhor, the Kapok tree is home to many birds and animals. If you cut it down, where will I find my dinner?"

Four tree porcupines swung down from branch to branch and whispered to the man: "Senhor, do you know what we animals and humans need in order to live? Oxygen. And, Senhor, do you know what trees produce? Oxygen! If you cut down the forests you will destroy that which gives us all life."

Several anteaters climbed down the Kapok tree with their young clinging to their backs. The unstriped anteater said to the sleeping man: "Senhor, you are chopping down this tree with no thought for the future. And surely you know that what happens tomorrow depends upon what you do today. The big man tells you to chop down a beautiful tree. He does not think of his own children, who tomorrow must live in a world without trees."

A three-toed sloth had begun climbing down from the canopy when the men first appeared. Only now did she reach the ground. Plodding ever so slowly over to the sleeping man, she spoke in her deep and lazy voice: "Senhor, how much is beauty worth? Can you live without it? If you destroy the beauty of the rain forest, on what would you feast your eyes?"

A child from the Yanomamo tribe who lived in the rain forest knelt over the sleeping man. He murmured in his ear: "Senhor, when you awake, please look upon us all with new eyes."

The man awoke with a start. Before him stood the rain forest child, and all around him, staring, were the creatures who depended upon the great Kapok tree. What wondrous and rare animals they were!

The man looked about and saw the sun streaming through the canopy. Spots of bright light glowed like jewels amidst the dark green forest. Strange and beautiful plants seemed to dangle in the air, suspended from the great Kapok tree.

The man smelled the fragrant perfume of their flowers. He felt the steamy mist rising from the forest floor. But he heard no sound, for the creatures were strangely silent.

The man stood and picked up his ax. He swung back his arm as though to strike the tree. Suddenly he stopped. He turned and looked at the animals and the child.

He hesitated. Then he dropped the ax
and walked out of the rain forest.

# Meet
# LYNNE CHERRY

"Keep everything that you have written," Lynne Cherry advises children who want to become writers. Her old stories and drawings probably smell like chocolate. She kept them all in a chocolate box for many years.

When she was growing up in Pennsylvania, Cherry spent time in the woods watching animals and nature. She remembers seeing the trees and fields disappear as new houses and roads appeared. These experiences helped her write *The Great Kapok Tree,* which takes place in a rain forest.

Lynne Cherry wants to "try to make the world a better place." One way she helps is by donating her artwork to groups that work to save the Earth.

# And my heart soars

The beauty of the trees,
the softness of the air,
the fragrance of the grass,
 speaks to me.

The summit of the mountain,
the thunder of the sky,
the rhythm of the sea,
 speaks to me.

The faintness of the stars,
the freshness of the morning,
the dew drop on the flower,
 speaks to me.

The strength of fire,
the taste of salmon,
the trail of the sun,
And the life that never goes away,
 They speak to me.

And my heart soars.

*Chief Dan George*

The British Columbia landscape surrounds Chief Dan George, a poet and member of the Salish nation.

# Keep It

**I Was Born in a Tree
and Raised by Bees**
by Jim Arnosky
Bradbury, 1988

Hello. My name is Crinkleroot. I was
born in a tree and raised by bees. I can
whistle in a hundred languages and speak
caterpillar, turtle, and salamander, too!

# Green!

## The Wump World

by Bill Peet
Houghton Mifflin, 1970

One morning the Wumps were awakened by a far-off humming sound. It seemed to be coming from somewhere above, and as the humming grew into a heavy roar, the sleepy-eyed Wumps crept through the trees for a peek at the sky.

# Meet John Javna

Two of John Javna's books zoomed to the top of the bestseller list in a very short time. The first was *50 Simple Things You Can Do to Save the Earth*. Close behind it was *50 Simple Things Kids Can Do to Save the Earth*. Javna was more than a little surprised at the success of his books. He explains that he is just an average person who happens to be "concerned with protecting the Earth for our children and future generations."

Javna's books were probably the first environmental handbooks that everyone could really understand. The writer says, "I want to make it easy for people to feel good about their ability to make a difference."

# SIMPLE THINGS KIDS CAN DO TO SAVE THE EARTH

The EarthWorks Group

Illustrated by Dave Jonason

John Javna, founder of the EarthWorks Group, believes that kids can make a difference. In his book, which is printed on recycled paper, he explains how doing simple things—like reusing paper bags—can add up to doing very big things—like saving trees.

As you read the facts and do the projects in this selection, remember that **you** and **you** and **you** can work together to save the Earth!

# USE IT AGAIN . . . AND AGAIN . . .

## TAKE A GUESS

*How many disposable plastic bottles do we use in four days?*

**A** Enough to fill a truck

**B** Enough to fill a warehouse

**C** As many as there are people in the whole U.S.

Long before you were born, back when your grandparents were kids, there was no such thing as a paper towel or a paper napkin. People used cloth. Back then, everything was used again and again. In fact, most people would never have imagined throwing something away after using it just once.

But today, we have lots of things that are made especially to be tossed in the garbage after one use; we call them "disposable." Aluminum foil, plastic bags, paper bags, plastic food wrap, and other products are all considered "disposable."

What's going on? Our Earth's treasures are being thrown out as trash. Wouldn't it be wonderful if everyone did a little something to stop this waste? Just imagine what a difference it would make!

*Answer: C. 240 million! Incredible!*

# DID YOU KNOW?

- We use millions of feet of paper towels every year. That's a lot of trees!
- Americans use 35 million paper clips every day.
- Americans buy 500 million disposable lighters every year. That's millions of pounds of plastic made by factories just so grown-ups can throw it away.

## What You Can Do

► Keep a cloth towel by the sink. Next time you rinse your hands or need to wipe up a spill, grab the cloth towel instead of a paper one.

► Keep a "rag bag" handy. Put your old, torn clothes in it, and you'll have a supply of rags to help you out with messy chores or art projects.

► Save plastic bags—you can use them again. If they're dirty, turn them inside out, rinse them and hang them up to dry.

► Aluminum foil is reusable. Wash it off, let it dry, and put it away. When it can't be used again, recycle it.

► Have you got some reusable food containers in your kitchen? (You know, the kind with snap-on tops.) Use them instead of just covering or wrapping food with plastic wrap.

► Start an Earth-positive lunchtime trend—use a lunch-box to carry your food to school. Or if you take a bag lunch, bring home the paper and plastic bags so you can reuse them.

## SEE FOR YOURSELF

Look around your house for some "disposable" things. Try to picture where they come from. Hold up a roll of paper towels and imagine it's a tree. Take a plastic bag or plastic wrap and try to see it as oil—or even better, a prehistoric creature. See aluminum foil as a precious metal from underground. They seem a lot more important now, don't they? They are!

# PRESTO, ON! . . . PRESTO, OFF!

## TAKE A GUESS

*You can save 20,000 gallons of water a year by not letting the water run. That's enough to fill:*

**A** A garbage can
**B** A big truck
**C** A swimming pool

Imagine pumping water or hauling it from a well every time you wanted to brush your teeth, like they used to in the old days. It was hard work!

Life is easier now. We can just turn on a faucet and . . . presto . . . water! In fact, it's so easy to get water that we let *gallons* of it go down the drain without thinking!

We need a little water-saving magic: Presto, on! . . . and Presto, off! Don't go with the flow!

Answer: C. You can save enough water to fill a swimming pool.

- Water comes out of the faucet faster than you think. For example: While you're waiting for water to get cold enough to have a drink, you could fill *six* half-gallon milk cartons!

- If you leave the water running while you brush your teeth, you can waste five gallons of water. That's enough to fill 53 cans of soda!

- If you leave the water running while you wash the dishes, you can waste 30 gallons of water—enough to wash a whole car!

# What You Can Do

► When you brush your teeth: Just wet your brush, then turn off the water . . . and then turn it on again when you need to rinse your brush off. You'll save up to nine gallons of water each time! That's enough to give your pet a bath.

► When you wash dishes: If you just fill up the basin and rinse dishes in it, instead of letting the water run, you can save up to 25 gallons each time. That's enough to take a five-minute shower.

► When you're going to take a bath: Plug the tub before you let the water run, so you don't waste any.

► When you're thirsty: If you like cool water, why not leave a bottle of it in the refrigerator instead of letting the water run? You'll save water, and still have a cool drink.

# SEE FOR YOURSELF

■ How long do you think it will take to fill a milk carton with water? To find out, get an empty half-gallon milk carton and a grown-up with a watch to time you.

■ Open the milk carton and hold it under the faucet.

■ Turn on the faucet and time it.

■ How long did it take to fill the carton? Imagine that all over the U.S., people are letting the water run like that. Don't be one of them!

P.S. Don't waste that water by pouring it down the sink—pour it on a thirsty plant instead. Good work!

## MAKE NEWS

*Which of these is the easiest to write a letter with?*

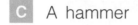

**A** A piece of chalk

**B** A pencil

**C** A hammer

Extra! Extra! Read all about it!
Where? In the newspaper.
Would you like to tell everyone what you think about saving the Earth? Why not write a letter to your local newspaper?

## DID YOU KNOW?

- Every day, $62\frac{1}{2}$ million newspapers are printed in America.

- Most of them have a special section called "Letters to the Editor." These letters are written to the newspaper by readers who have ideas they want to share.

- The newspapers print the letters because they feel it is important for people to voice their opinions.

- Usually, the letters are written by adults. But every once in a while, a kid will write. When that happens, people pay special attention to it; kids have a special way of looking at the world.

Answer: We're not telling. But please don't try to write a letter with a hammer.

# What You Can Do

► Write a letter to your local paper. Tell them what you're doing to save our world. Or tell them what you wish everyone would do—and why.

► Start the letter with "Dear Editor." And when you finish it, be sure to add your name and address and phone number.

► Ask an adult to help you get the newspaper's address. Usually, you can find it on the "Letters to the Editor" page.

► If the newspaper doesn't print your letter, don't give up. Keep writing. The more times you write, the more chances there are that one of your letters will be printed.

► If that happens, many people will be able to read it. And they'll learn something important about saving the Earth.

*At School:* Suggest that your class write to the newspaper.

■ You can have a discussion about saving the Earth.

■ Then you can write a group letter together and sign it "From the _____ class at _____ school."

■ Or each person can write her or his own letter and your class can send the letters all together.

The Kids' EarthWorks Group
1400 Shattuck Avenue, #25
Berkeley, CA 94709

3-2-1 Contact
1 Lincoln Plaza
New York, NY 10023

Ranger Rick
National Wildlife Federation
8925 Leesburg Pike
Vienna, VA 22184-30001

You can also write to magazines and even to the Kids' EarthWorks Group!

Dear Editor,
    When other people throw out their
newspapers, I pick them up and bring them
into the house. I go to the hardware store and
buy pieces of rope. Then I tie the newspapers
with the rope. When the garbage truck comes,
I give the paper to the people who work on the
truck. They take the newspapers to a place
where they can be recycled.
    It's important for people to recycle paper
so that we have more trees and oxygen.
        Sincerely,
        Billy Sirico, Age 8½

Dear Editor,
    I recycle bags in
school, at home, and when
I go places on vacation.
After I go shopping with
my mother, I help put the
food in the refrigerator.
Then I take the bags and
put them in my living
room closet. When I need
a bag for my lunch, I use
one of the bags from the
closet. I also use the bags
to put my toys in.
        Sincerely,
        Chris Rodriguez, Age 8½

Dear Editor,
    I think people should bring a plastic
bag or a cloth bag to the beach with them.
They can put their garbage in the bag.
Then they can throw the garbage away in
the garbage can, and they can save the
bag to use again. This will help the ocean
from getting polluted, and the animals
will have a clean ocean.
        Sincerely,
        Stasha Maharaj, Age 9

73

# THE STREETS ARE FREE

by Kurusa

illustrated by Sandra Speidel

Not very long ago, when Carlitos's grandfather was a boy, mountain lions roamed the hills of Venezuela. One particular mountain was covered with forests and bushes, small creeks and dirt paths. Every morning the mist would reach down and touch the flowers and the butterflies.

On the hill above the town of Caracas, where Cheo, Carlitos, and Camila now live, there was just one house. It was a simple house made of mud and dried leaves from sugar cane and banana plants. In the mornings, when the family went to fetch water, they often saw lion's tracks in the soft earth. Later, they would stop by the creeks to catch sardines for dinner.

Years passed and more people came from towns and villages all over Venezuela to make their homes on the mountainside.

They built their houses of wood and the children played among the trees, in the creeks and on the open fields.

The forest began to grow towards the new village, and the village began to grow towards the forest.

The dirt road that led to the big city was soon covered with asphalt.

And more people came.

There were so many houses that they reached right to the top of the mountain where the lion tracks used to be. The creeks became sewers. The dirt paths were littered with garbage. The mountain became a very poor town called the 'barrio' San José.

The children who used to play in the open fields could no longer play there, nor in the forest, nor in the streams.

The fields in the valleys were now filled with office towers. The whole mountain was covered with houses.

The main road became a highway. There were only a few trees and not one flower. The children had nowhere to play.

After school, Cheo, Carlitos, and Camila went to a house that was converted into a library. There they read books and played with clay and paints and board games and all kinds of interesting things. But they had nowhere to play hopscotch, or soccer, or baseball, or tag.

After they left the library, they played in the street.

One day, while they were playing leapfrog, a grocery truck came barrelling down the street. The driver shouted:

"Get out of the way! Let me through!"

"The streets are free," said the boys. But the truck was much bigger and more powerful than the children. So they walked to the top of the mountain to fly their kites. In about half an hour, every one of the kites was tangled in the hydro wires.

The children went back down the mountain to play ball. But the ball kept getting lost in people's washing and trapped on roof tops.

One woman ran out of her house when the children were trying to fetch the ball.

"Get out of here," she shouted, "or I'll hit you with my broom."

"The streets are free," said the youngest boy. But the children knew they had better leave her alone.

Dejected, they went to the library. They sat down on the steps and thought.

"There must be somewhere we can play," said Camila.

"Let's go see the mayor and tell him we need somewhere to play," suggested another.

"Where does he live?" asked Carlitos, the smallest boy. The children looked at each other. Nobody knew.

"Let's go to City Hall. That can't be too far away."

"But we can't go there without adults. They won't listen to us at City Hall," said Camila with big, sad eyes.

"Then let's ask our parents."

So the children went from house to house to ask their parents to go with them to City Hall. But their parents were cooking, sewing, washing, repairing, away working, in other words . . . busy.

The children returned to the library steps. They just sat there and felt very sad.

Then the librarian appeared.

"Why all the sad faces?" he asked.

The children told him.

"What do you want to tell the mayor?"

"We want a playground."

"Do you know where?"

"Yes," said Carlitos, "in an empty lot near the bottom of the mountain."

"Do you know what it should look like?"

"Well . . . "

"Why don't you come inside and discuss it?"

They talked for more than an hour. Cheo, the oldest boy, took notes on a large pad.

"Good," said the librarian, "and now what do you want to do?"

"We're still in the same boat," said Camila. "What good is a piece of paper if the adults don't go with us to see the mayor?"

"Won't they go with you?"

"They won't even listen to us," Camila said.

"Have you tried going alone?"

"Well, no."

"So, what do you want to do?"

The children looked at each other.

"Let's make a banner," said Cheo.

They all worked together and made a sign that said:

81

# WE HAVE NO
# WE NEED A

"Tomorrow we'll plan the details," said the librarian, and he left for the chess club.

The children put the finishing touches on their sign.

"It's perfect like this!"

They rolled up the sign and the large list with their notes.

"We're ready," they said.

Again the children looked at each other.

"Why don't we go right now?" a few children said at the same time.

With the banner and the large list of notes rolled up under their arms, the children of San José walked to City Hall.

# WHERE TO PLAY PLAYGROUND

City Hall was even bigger than they imagined. The doorway was very high. Standing in the middle of it was a big, fat man.

"No one comes in here," he said.

"We came to ask for a playground."

"We came to see the people at City Hall. We need a playground."

"But the people at the Council don't want to see you. Go home or I'll call the police."

"Look, this is the kind of playground we want," said Carlitos, innocently, and he unrolled the paper with their notes on it.

Camila said, "We need somewhere to play," and she unrolled the banner.

"Get out of here!" shouted the fat man.

"The streets are free!" Cheo shouted back, and he sat down.

"We're not going to move until they listen to us," said another boy. "In the library they told us that City Hall is here to listen to us."

Back in San José, the mothers were worried. They couldn't find their children. Somebody said she saw them leaving the library with some big sheets of paper.

"Oh no," mumbled the librarian. "I think I know where they are."

The fat man in the doorway of City Hall was yelling so much his face was turning redder and redder. A crowd gathered around City Hall to see what all the fuss was about.

Then everything happened at once.

The mothers, the librarian, and the police all arrived at City Hall at the same time.

The mothers shouted, "What are you doing?"

"Take them away!" shouted the fat man to the police. "They're disturbing the peace." The policemen started pulling the children by their arms.

"Excuse me," the librarian raised one hand, "but what is going on here?"

"They won't let us talk to anyone about our playground," said Carlitos.

"The police are going to arrest them and put them in jail for their bad behaviour," said the fat man.

Then one mother who was even bigger and fatter than he stood in front of the children.

"Oh no, you don't," she said. "If you put a hand on these kids, you have to arrest me, too."

"And me, too," said another mother.

"And me," shouted the rest of the mothers.

Suddenly, standing in the doorway of City Hall, were the mayor, a reporter, and a municipal engineer.

"What's going on here?" the mayor asked.

"We need a playground."

"They want to arrest us."

"Those people are starting a riot."

They were all talking at once.

"Let the children speak," the librarian suggested.

"Yes, I'd like to talk to the children," said the reporter, getting out her notebook. They told her their story.

When they were finished, the mayor turned to the municipal engineer. "Is there space for them to have a playground?"

"Yes!" the children shouted together. "We know where. We can show you."

"Why don't you come and see it?" asked the librarian.

"Um—," said the engineer.

"Uhmmmmmmm—," said the mayor. "Tomorrow. Tomorrow we'll look at it. I don't have time now. I'm very busy. But tomorrow, tomorrow for sure. Ahem. Remember, we are here to serve you." Then the mayor shook hands with all the mothers.

"I knew it," said Camila.

"I would very much like to go with you," said the reporter. So the children, the mothers, the librarian, and the reporter all went to see the empty lot.

"What do you want the playground to look like?" the reporter asked. The children began to read their list. The reporter took lots of notes and wrote down everything on their sign:

We need a playground
with trees
and shrubs
and flower seeds
 swings
 an old tractor to climb on
 and sticks to dig with
A house for dolls
 a lasso to play cowboys
Lots of room for baseball,
 volleyball and soccer,
 to have races and
  fly kites,
 to play leapfrog, tag,
 kick-the-can,
blind man's bluff
 and hide and seek
grass to roll on
 and do gymnastics
A patio to play on
 and a bench
for our parents
 to sit and visit.

THE END

The next day, the library was empty. The children sat on the steps.

"I think," sighed Camila, "I think that nothing's going to happen."

"What if we went to City Hall again with our big brothers and sisters?" asked Carlitos.

"They'll put us in jail," Camila said.

A week passed.

One day, the librarian appeared in the doorway smiling. He was holding a newspaper with a huge headline:

# THE CHILDREN OF SAN JOSÉ TAKE ON CITY HALL
## They ask for special park
## The mayor doesn't come through

"That's us!" said Cheo.

"We're famous!" laughed Carlitos.

"Yeah, but they're still not going to do anything," said Camila.

She was wrong. The same afternoon, the mayor, the municipal engineer and three assistants came to the barrio.

"We came to see the land for the playground. Soon we'll give it to you," they said proudly.

"Very soon," said the engineer.

"Very, very soon," smiled the mayor.

Then it happened: One morning, the assistants tied a red ribbon across the entrance to the empty lot. At twelve o'clock sharp, the mayor, dressed very elegantly and with freshly shined shoes, came and cut the ribbon with an extra-large pair of scissors.

"I get it," said Camila. "There's an election soon, isn't there? After the big ceremony, I bet nothing will happen."

This time Camila was right. Weeks passed and the engineers never came back. The empty lot that was supposed to be the playground was just collecting garbage. Little by little, the adults forgot about it. But the children didn't.

"What happened to our playground?" the children asked. The adults always gave the same answer:

"The politicians always promise but they never do anything."

Carlitos, Camila, and Cheo weren't satisfied. They sat on the edge of the mountain and looked down at the empty lot and thought about it all. Then Carlitos said:

"Why can't we have a playground anyway?"

"Are you crazy? It's very complicated."

"But if everybody helped, maybe . . . "

It was a crazy idea, but the young children started talking to their friends, who talked to their older brothers and sisters, who talked to their mothers, and the mothers talked to the fathers.

One day, Carlitos heard his uncle and some friends arguing about the playground. His uncle banged the table. He said they could easily build the playground themselves—they didn't need the council. But his friends were not so sure.

"Don't be crazy. Nobody cooperates here, not even to clean up the sidewalk! How could you get everyone to build them a playground?"

"No, buddy, everyone knows each other. They'll help," said Carlitos's uncle.

"Forget it. You'll end up building it yourself."

"Alone? No. I'll help you," said one of the men.

"I will, too."

Time passed and more and more people talked about the idea. The neighbourhood committee organized a public meeting one Saturday. About fifty people came. The discussion lasted four hours and was very loud.

"We can't do it," said some.

"We can do it," said others.

There seemed no way to agree. Carlitos's uncle and the children passionately defended the idea, but most of the parents doubted it could be done without the politicians' help. After all the shouting, there was silence. It looked like the meeting was going to end that way until one mother remembered she had some planks of wood she didn't need. One father said he was a carpenter. One girl timidly said, "In my house we have some rope to make a swing with."

Everybody became very enthusiastic and suddenly they all had suggestions.

"I want to bring some nails," insisted one grandmother.

Carlitos, Cheo, and Camila all started jumping up and down.

"It's really going to happen!"

All the neighbours began to build the playground. They brought cement and bricks and buckets and sheets of aluminum and sandbags and old tires and wooden boards of every size.

They nailed and hammered and dug holes and planted and sanded. They all worked in their spare time.

On the wire fence the children put up a sign they made themselves:

SAN JOSÉ PLAYGROUND
EVERYBODY COME AND PLAY

# Meet Kurusa

Kurusa has spent over twelve years in her native Venezuela working with children in cultural and social programs. *The Streets Are Free* reflects some of her experiences with the children who use the public library in San José de La Urbina, a town on the edge of Caracas.

In her work promoting reading and children's literature in Venezuela, Kurusa has organized a bookmobile service and founded a publishing house for children's books.

The author lives in Caracas with her three children. She loves sailing and animals, and she has a sailboat with red sails on which a favorite seagull lives.

# Preserven el Parque Elysian

## by Mike Kellin

1. ¡Qué lin - do el par - que E - ly - sian! _____ ¡Qué
lin - do el par - que E - ly - sian! _____ ¡Qué
lin - do! (¡Qué lin - do!) ¡Qué lin - do! (¡Qué lin - do!) ¡Qué
lin - do el par - que E - ly - sian! _____

1. ¡Qué lindo el parque Elysian!
2. ¡Me gusta el parque Elysian!

3. ¡El aire es libre, amigos!
4. ¡No queremos fincas en el parque!
5. ¡Queremos el zacate verde!
6. ¡El parque es suyo y mío!
7. ¡Los niños necesitan el parque!
8. ¡Preserven el parque Elysian!
9. ¡NO PASARÁN LOS BULLDOZERS!

1. Elysian Park is beautiful!
2. Elysian Park is my kind of park!
3. The air is free, my friends!
4. We don't want building in the park!
5. We want the green grass!
6. The park is yours and mine!
7. The children need the park!

8. Save Elysian Park!
9. STOP THE BULLDOZERS!

Illustration, by José Ortega, of musicians playing instruments commonly used in South America: bongo drums, a panpipe, and a charango.

99

# CONTENTS

UNIT
**2**

WEATHER THE STORM

# WEATHER

Whether the weather be fine
Or whether the weather be not.
Whether the weather be cold
Or whether the weather be hot.
We'll weather the weather
Whatever the weather,
Whether we like it or not.

A NANDI TALE

# BRINGING THE RAIN TO KAPITI PLAIN

BRINGING THE RAIN TO KAPITI PLAIN *by Verna Aardema / pictures by Beatriz Vidal*

RETOLD BY VERNA AARDEMA
PICTURES BY BEATRIZ VIDAL

This is the great
    Kapiti Plain,
All fresh and green
    from the African rains—
A sea of grass for the
    ground birds to nest in,
And patches of shade for
    wild creatures to rest in;
With acacia trees for
    giraffes to browse on,
And grass for the herdsmen
    to pasture their cows on.

But one year the rains
    were so very belated,
That all of the big wild
    creatures migrated.
Then Ki-pat helped to end
    that terrible drought—
And this story tells
    how it all came about!

This is the cloud,
    all heavy with rain,
That shadowed the ground
    on Kapiti Plain.

This is the grass,
    all brown and dead,
That needed the rain
    from the cloud overhead—
The big, black cloud,
    all heavy with rain,
That shadowed the ground
    on Kapiti Plain.

These are the cows,
    all hungry and dry,
Who mooed for the rain
    to fall from the sky;
To green-up the grass,
    all brown and dead,
That needed the rain
    from the cloud overhead—
The big, black cloud,
    all heavy with rain,
That shadowed the ground
    on Kapiti Plain.

This is Ki-pat,
    who watched his herd
As he stood on one leg,
    like the big stork bird;
Ki-pat, whose cows
    were so hungry and dry,
They mooed for the rain
    to fall from the sky;
To green-up the grass,
    all brown and dead,
That needed the rain
    from the cloud overhead—
The big, black cloud,
    all heavy with rain,
That shadowed the ground
    on Kapiti Plain.

This is the eagle
   who dropped a feather,
A feather that helped
   to change the weather.
It fell near Ki-pat,
   who watched his herd
As he stood on one leg,
   like the big stork bird;
Ki-pat, whose cows
   were so hungry and dry,

They mooed for the rain
   to fall from the sky;
To green-up the grass,
   all brown and dead,
That needed the rain
   from the cloud overhead—
The big, black cloud,
   all heavy with rain,
That shadowed the ground
   on Kapiti Plain.

This is the arrow
    Ki-pat put together,
With a slender stick
    and an eagle feather;
From the eagle who happened
    to drop a feather,
A feather that helped
    to change the weather.

It fell near Ki-pat,
    who watched his herd
As he stood on one leg,
    like the big stork bird;
Ki-pat, whose cows
    were so hungry and dry,
They mooed for the rain
    to fall from the sky;
To green-up the grass,
    all brown and dead,
That needed the rain
    from the cloud overhead—
The big, black cloud,
    all heavy with rain,
That shadowed the ground
    on Kapiti Plain.

This is the bow,
    so long and strong,
And strung with a string,
    a leather thong;
A bow for the arrow
    Ki-pat put together,
With a slender stick
    and an eagle feather;
From the eagle who happened
    to drop a feather,
A feather that helped
    to change the weather.

It fell near Ki-pat,
    who watched his herd
As he stood on one leg,
    like the big stork bird;
Ki-pat, whose cows
    were so hungry and dry,
They mooed for the rain
    to fall from the sky;
To green-up the grass,
    all brown and dead,
That needed the rain
    from the cloud overhead—
The big, black cloud,
    all heavy with rain,
That shadowed the ground
    on Kapiti Plain.

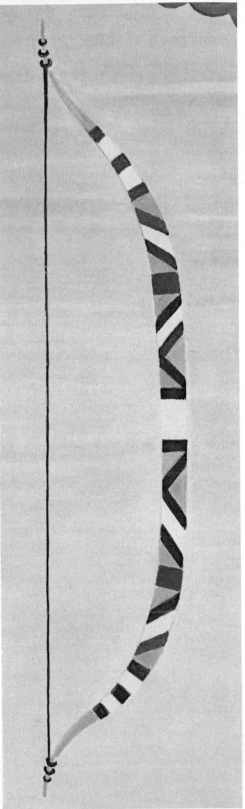

This was the shot
    that pierced the cloud
And loosed the rain
    with thunder LOUD!
A shot from the bow,
    so long and strong,
And strung with a string,
    a leather thong;
A bow for the arrow
    Ki-pat put together,
With a slender stick
    and an eagle feather;
From the eagle who happened
    to drop a feather,
A feather that helped
    to change the weather.

It fell near Ki-pat,
    who watched his herd
As he stood on one leg,
    like the big stork bird;
Ki-pat, whose cows
    were so hungry and dry,
They mooed for the rain
    to fall from the sky;
To green-up the grass,
    all brown and dead,
That needed the rain
    from the cloud overhead—
The big, black cloud,
    all heavy with rain,
That shadowed the ground
    on Kapiti Plain.

So the grass grew green,
    and the cattle fat!
And Ki-pat got a wife
    and a little Ki-pat—

Who tends the cows now,
    and shoots down the rain,
When black clouds shadow
    Kapiti Plain.

# MEET

VERNA AARDEMA

If you remember the old rhyme "The House that Jack Built," you probably know where Verna Aardema got the idea for *Bringing the Rain to Kapiti Plain.* When she first tried to write the rhyme, Aardema got stuck. "I lay awake that night thinking about it. At four o'clock, the first stanza jelled in my mind. The next afternoon the rest of it came rolling off my typewriter."

Many other award-winning titles have "rolled off" Aardema's typewriter. Two of the best-known are *Who's in Rabbit's House?* and *Why Mosquitoes Buzz in People's Ears,* which were chosen as Notable Children's Books by the American Library Association.

Why Mosquitoes Buzz in People's Ears
Verna Aardema | pictures by
Leo and Diane Dillon

Verna Aardema
Who's in Rabbit's House?
pictures by Leo and Diane Dillon

# IN TIME OF Silver Rain

In time of silver rain
The earth
Puts forth new life again,
Green grasses grow
And flowers lift their heads,
And over all the plain
The wonder spreads
        Of life,
        Of life,
        Of life!

In time of silver rain
The butterflies
Lift silken wings
To catch a rainbow cry,
And trees put forth
New leaves to sing
In joy beneath the sky
As down the roadway
Passing boys and girls
Go singing, too,
In time of silver rain
        When spring
        And life
        Are new.

*Langston Hughes*

124

# ALERT

by Franklyn M. Branley
illustrated by Paul Selwyn

Tornadoes are powerful storms.

On a tornado day the air is hot and still. Clouds
build up rapidly. They get thick and dark. In the
distance there is thunder and lightning, rain and hail.

Here and there parts of the clouds seem to reach
toward the ground. Should these parts grow larger
and become funnel shaped, watch out. The funnels
could become tornadoes.

The funnel of a tornado is usually dark gray or black. It may also be yellowish or red.

The colors come from red and yellow dirt picked up by the tornado as it moves along the ground.

Tornadoes can strike most anywhere, but usually they happen where there is a lot of flat land. Most tornadoes occur in Texas, Oklahoma, Kansas, Nebraska, Iowa, and Missouri. Florida also has a lot of tornadoes.

Tornadoes can touch down over seas and lakes. When that happens, they are called waterspouts.

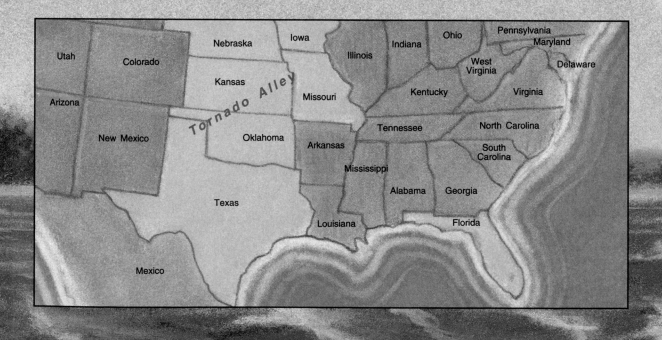

Most tornadoes occur during April, May, and June. That's when cold air meets warm air near the Earth's surface. The cold air pushes under the warm air. The warm air is lighter than the cold air and rises rapidly.

As the warm air moves upward, it spins around, or twists. That's why tornadoes are sometimes called twisters. Some people call them cyclones. The wind speed around the funnel of the tornado may reach 300 miles an hour. No other wind on Earth blows that fast.

As the hot air rises, it also spreads out. It makes a funnel of air, with the small part of the funnel touching the ground and the large part in the dark clouds. Air all around the tornado moves in toward the funnel. At the same time, storm winds push the twisting funnel, moving it along the Earth.

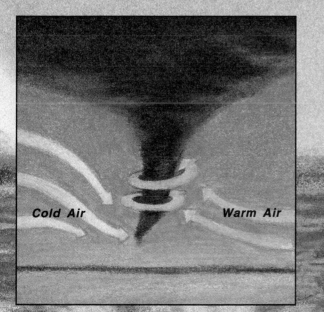

Cold Air          Warm Air

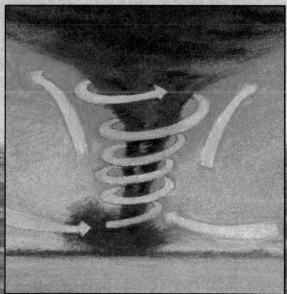

During tornado season in the United States, there may be 40 or 50 tornadoes in one week. Sometimes there are many more. Most are small. Usually a tornado blows itself out in less than an hour. Some last only a few seconds.

Small tornadoes don't travel far, and they cause little damage. Big tornadoes destroy everything in their paths. They may travel 200 miles and last several hours.

During a tornado there is thunder and lightning, rain and hail. And there is lots of noise. It can sound as loud as a freight train or a jet engine. The word *tornado* comes from a Latin word that means thunder. Some of the noise does come from thunder, but most of it comes from the roaring wind. There is lots of noise, and lots and lots of wind.

Tornadoes are very powerful, and some cause a lot of damage. Tornadoes can pick up branches and boards, stones and bricks, cars, and sometimes even people.

They can rip off roofs and leave a trail of wrecked houses. A tornado's path may be only 20 or 30 feet wide. Or it might be 1,000 feet or more—maybe even a mile.

In 1931 a tornado in Minnesota lifted a train off its tracks. The train and its passengers were carried through the air and dropped 80 feet from the tracks. There were 170 people on board. Though many people were hurt, only one person was killed. But in 1974 a series of tornadoes in Missouri, Illinois, Indiana, and 10 other states killed 315 people in 24 hours.

129

Scientists keep a close watch during tornado season. They use satellites that see storms developing. And there is radar to detect tornadoes.

Tornado spotters are people who watch for tornadoes. They tell radio and television stations to warn people about tornadoes while the twisters are still far away. The warnings tell people to go to a safe spot, where the tornado can't hurt them.

TORNADO ALERT

If a tornado is on its way, here's what you should do. Go to a nearby storm cellar. Storm cellars are underground rooms with heavy doors. They are safe.

If you are in a mobile home, get out of it. A tornado can rip apart a mobile home, even when it is tied down with strong cables. Lie face down in a ditch and cover your head with your hands. When you're in a ditch, sticks and stones flying through the air can't hit you.

If you are in a house, go to the basement and crouch under the stairs or under a heavy workbench. Or go to a closet that is far from an outside wall. Be sure to keep far away from windows. The wind could smash them and send splinters of glass through the air.

If you are in school, follow directions. Your teacher will take you to a basement or to an inside hall. Crouch on your knees near an inner wall. Bend over and clasp your hands behind your head. Most important, keep away from glass windows.

If you are out in the country in a car, don't try to race the tornado. Get out, and find a ditch to lie in.

When there's a tornado, there is also thunder and lightning. So keep away from metal things and from anything that uses electricity. Lightning can travel along metal pipes, and also along electric and telephone wires.

Listen to a battery radio. The radio will tell you when the storm has passed by. Stay where you are safe until you are sure the tornado is over.

Tornadoes are scary. Even if you are not right in the funnel, there is heavy rain all around, dark skies, thunder, lightning, and lots of wind. Often there will be hailstones. They may be as big as golf balls, or even bigger.

Don't panic. Know what to do when there is a tornado. And know where to go.

There is no way to stop tornadoes. But you can be safe from them when you know what to do.

## Tornado Rules

- Don't panic.
- Listen.
- Look.
- Follow Directions.

# MEET
# FRANKLYN M. BRANLEY

When Franklyn Branley began to teach grade school, he noticed that there were not very many good science books for children. He decided to write some himself. He began the *Let's-Read-and-Find-Out* series and wrote more than thirty books for it about the moon, the stars, rockets, and many other science topics.

Branley wrote *Tornado Alert* for a specific reason. "It's important that everyone knows there are such things as tornadoes and that people can protect themselves." Some people have said that his books are too scary, but Branley believes they give information children need to know.

# Fair Weather...

**Beacons of Light: Lighthouses**

by Gail Gibbons

Morrow, 1990

**Very Last First Time**

by Jan Andrews

illustrated by Ian Wallace

Atheneum, 1985

or Foul?

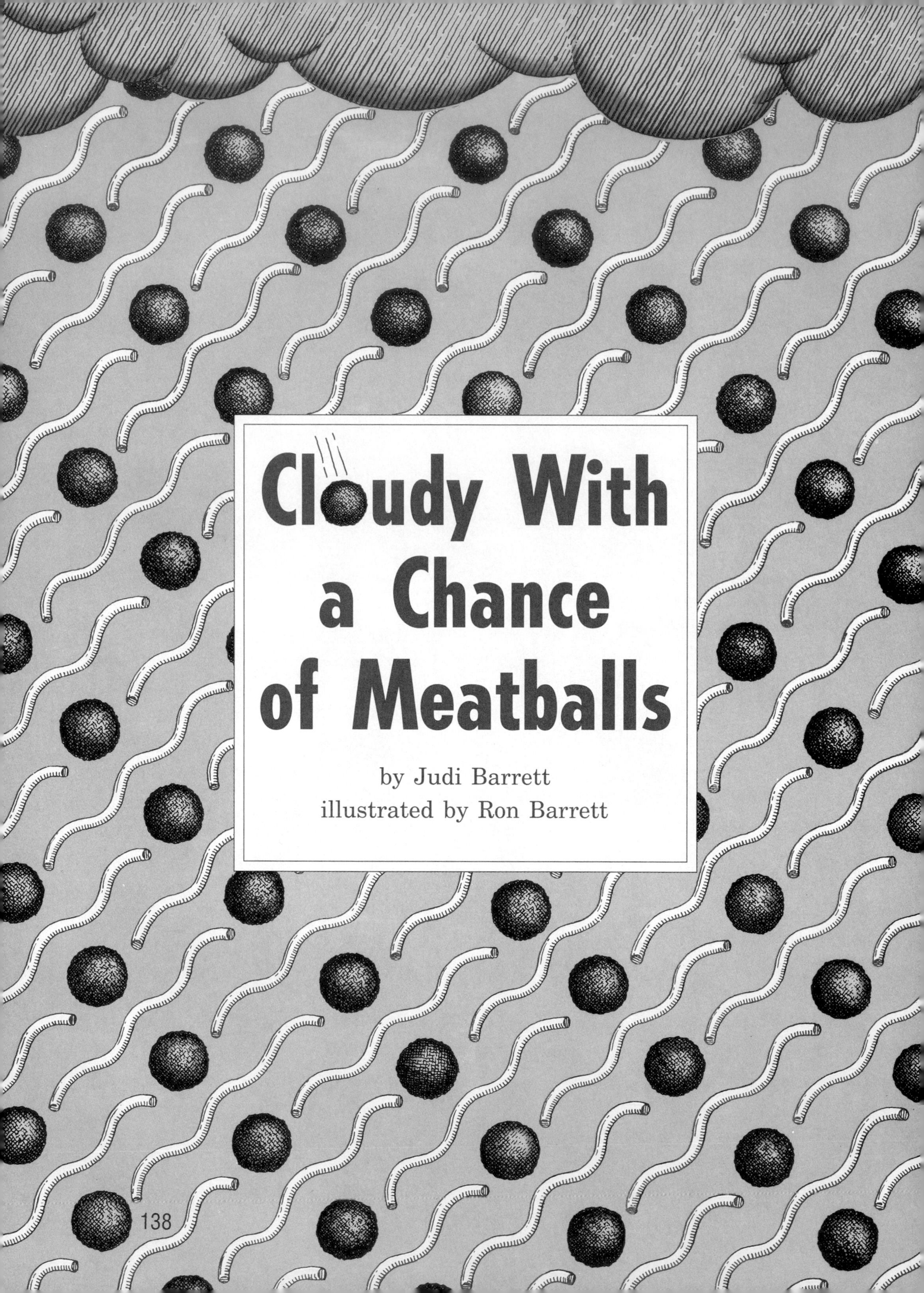

# Cloudy With a Chance of Meatballs

by Judi Barrett

illustrated by Ron Barrett

We were all sitting around the big kitchen table. It was Saturday morning. Pancake morning. Mom was squeezing oranges for juice. Henry and I were betting on how many pancakes we each could eat. And Grandpa was doing the flipping.

Seconds later, something flew through the air headed toward
the kitchen ceiling . . .

. . . and landed right on Henry.

After we realized that the flying object was only a pancake, we all
laughed, even Grandpa.
Breakfast continued quite
uneventfully. All the other
pancakes landed in the
pan. And all of them
were eaten, even the
one that landed
on Henry.

That night, touched off by the pancake incident at breakfast, Grandpa told us the best tall-tale bedtime story he'd ever told.

"Across an ocean, over lots of huge bumpy mountains, across three hot deserts, and one smaller ocean . . .

. . . there lay the tiny town
of Chewandswallow.

In most ways, it was very much like any other tiny town. It had a Main Street lined with stores, houses with trees and gardens around them, a schoolhouse, about three hundred people, and some assorted cats and dogs.

But there were no food stores in the town of Chewandswallow. They didn't need any. The sky supplied all the food they could possibly want.

The only thing that was really different about Chewandswallow was its weather. It came three times a day, at breakfast, lunch, and dinner. Everything that everyone ate came from the sky.

Whatever the weather served, that was what they ate.

But it never rained rain. It never snowed snow. And it never blew just wind. It rained things like soup and juice. It snowed mashed potatoes and green peas. And sometimes the wind blew in storms of hamburgers.

The people could watch the weather report on television in the morning and they would even hear a prediction for the next day's food.

When the townspeople went outside, they carried their plates, cups, glasses, forks, spoons, knives, and napkins with them. That way they would always be prepared for any kind of weather.

If there were leftovers, and there usually were, the people took them home and put them in their refrigerators in case they got hungry between meals.

The menu varied.

By the time they woke up in the morning, breakfast was coming down.

After a brief shower of orange juice, low clouds of sunny-side-up eggs moved in followed by pieces of toast.

Butter and jelly sprinkled down for the toast. And most of the time it rained milk afterwards.

For lunch one day, frankfurters, already in their rolls, blew in from the northwest at about five miles an hour.

There were mustard clouds nearby. Then the wind shifted to the east and brought in baked beans.

A drizzle of soda finished off the meal.

Dinner one night consisted of lamb chops, becoming heavy at times, with occasional ketchup. Periods of peas and baked potatoes were followed by gradual clearing, with a wonderful Jell-O setting in the west.

The Sanitation Department of Chewandswallow had a rather unusual job for a sanitation department. It had to remove the food that fell on the houses and sidewalks and lawns. The workers cleaned things up after every meal and fed all the dogs and cats. Then they emptied some of it into the surrounding oceans for the fish and turtles and whales to eat. The rest of the food was put back into the earth so that the soil would be richer for the people's
flower gardens.

Life for the townspeople was delicious until the weather took a turn for the worse.

One day there was nothing but Gorgonzola cheese all day long.

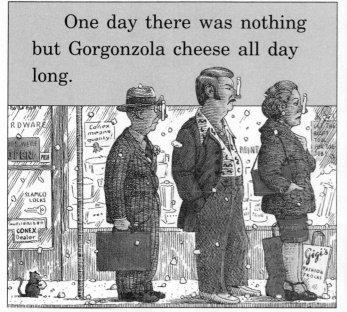

The next day there was only broccoli, all overcooked.

And the next day there were Brussels sprouts and peanut butter with mayonnaise.

Another day there was a pea soup fog. No one could see where they were going and they could barely find the rest of the meal that got stuck in the fog.

The food was getting larger and larger, and so were the portions. The people were getting frightened. Violent storms blew up frequently. Awful things were happening.

One Tuesday there was a hurricane of bread and rolls all day long and into the night. There were soft rolls and hard rolls, some with seeds and some without. There was white bread and rye and whole wheat toast. Most of it was larger than they had ever seen bread and rolls before. It was a terrible day. Everyone had to stay indoors. Roofs were damaged, and the Sanitation Department was beside itself. The mess took the workers four days to clean up, and the sea was full of floating rolls.

To help out, the people piled up as much bread as they could in their backyards. The birds picked at it a bit, but it just stayed there and got staler and staler.

There was a storm of
pancakes one morning and
a downpour of maple syrup
that nearly flooded the town.
A huge pancake covered the
school. No one could get
it off because of its weight,
so they had to close the
school.

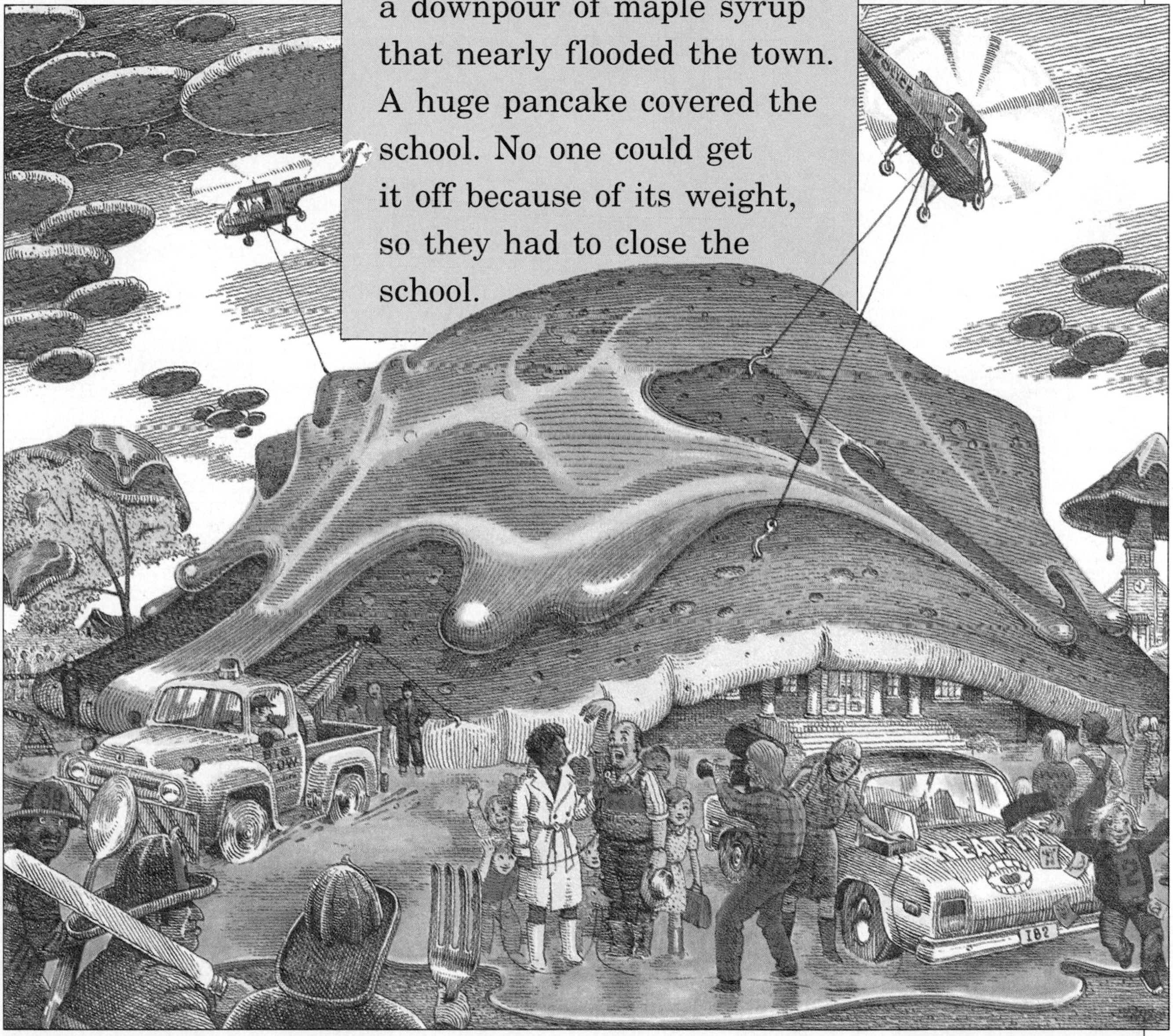

Lunch one day brought fifteen-inch drifts of cream cheese and jelly sandwiches. Everyone ate themselves sick and the day ended with a stomachache.

There was an awful salt and pepper wind accompanied by an even worse tomato tornado. People were sneezing themselves silly and running to avoid the tomatoes. The town was a mess. There were seeds and pulp everywhere.

The Sanitation Department gave up. The job was too big.

Everyone feared for their lives. They couldn't go outside most of the time. Many houses had been badly damaged by giant meatballs, stores were boarded up and there was no more school for the children.

So a decision was made to abandon the town of Chewandswallow. It was a matter of survival.

The people glued together the giant pieces of stale bread sandwich-style with peanut butter...

. . . took the absolute necessities with them, and set sail on their rafts for a new land.

After being afloat for a week, they finally reached a small coastal town, which welcomed them. The bread had held up surprisingly well, well enough for them to build temporary houses for themselves out of it.

The children began school again, and the adults all tried to find places for themselves in the new land. The biggest change they had to make was getting used to buying food at a supermarket. They found it odd that the food was kept on shelves, packaged in boxes, cans and bottles. Meat that had to be cooked was kept in large refrigerators. Nothing came down from the sky except rain and snow. The clouds above their heads were not made of fried eggs. No one ever got hit by a hamburger again.

And nobody dared to go back to Chewandswallow to find out what had happened to it. They were too afraid."

Henry and I were awake until the very end of Grandpa's story. I remember his good-night kiss.

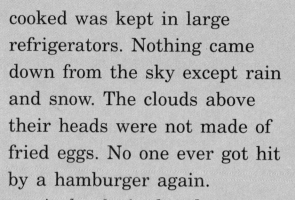

The next morning we woke up to see snow falling outside our window.

We ran downstairs for breakfast and ate it a little faster than usual so we could go sledding with Grandpa.

It's funny, but even as we were sliding down the hill we thought we saw a giant pat of butter at the top, and we could almost smell mashed potatoes.

## Meet Judi Barrett

Judi Barrett has always had lots of imagination. When she was a child, she loved to make things. She made little people out of peanuts, horses out of pipe cleaners, and dolls out of old quilts.

As an adult, she has used her imagination for writing books, such as *Animals Should Definitely Not Wear Clothing, Benjamin's 365 Birthdays,* and *Cloudy With a Chance of Meatballs.*

Judi Barrett also gets very involved in the art for her books. "I see my books visually while I write them," she says. "The words come along with images of what the book should look like, the feeling it should have."

## Meet Ron Barrett

What made Ron Barrett want to draw? It was those silly little characters in the comic books his father used to leave on the table. Ron Barrett remembers all the characters who lived "stacked up in the little boxes on the funny pages."

Ron has kept his sense of humor. Here is what he says about his pictures for *Cloudy With a Chance of Meatballs*: "The book took one year to design and draw. I used a very small pen. Hamburgers and pancakes actually posed for the pictures. I ate my models."

*The weather on Earth can be hot or it can be cold, but the weather on the other eight planets is truly "out of this world"!*

VISIT SUNNY MERCURY

OUT OF

### Mercury

Don't expect cool breezes on Mercury— at least not on the side facing the sun. Temperatures will be zooming up to 800°F (427°C).

### Venus

As usual, the forecast for Venus is cloudy with a chance of rain. Expect temperatures close to 850°F (454°C).

### Earth

As always, the weather on Earth is mixed. Expect a low of -120°F (-49°C) in Antarctica and a high of 130°F (54°C) in Libya.

### Mars

On Mars, tornado-like winds are blanketing the whole planet with clouds of pink dust. Tonight's low should be -204°F (-96°C).

# THIS WORLD

## Jupiter

Once again, Jupiter's cloud cover is thick, and the Great Red Spot storm system is still the size of three Earths. The temperature is -236°F (-113°C).

## Saturn

Saturn will have winds of up to 1,000 miles (1,609 km) per hour today. (Earth's hurricane winds can be 100 miles per hour.) Expect cloud-top temperatures of -285°F (-141°C).

## Uranus

No surprises today. The forecast is for continued cold on icy Uranus. The surface temperature will be close to -350°F (-177°C).

## Neptune

At -261°F (-127°C), Neptune is warmer than its neighbors. Winds of up to 1,500 miles per hour (2,414 km) could make you feel pretty chilly, though.

## Pluto

On faraway Pluto, temperatures will be -369°F (-187°C). But what can you expect from a planet made of frozen gas, ice, and rock?

VISIT PLUTO IT'S COOL

## Spring Rain

The storm came up so very quick
    It couldn't have been quicker.
I should have brought my hat along,
    I should have brought my slicker.

My hair is wet, my feet are wet,
    I couldn't be much wetter.
I fell into a river once
    But this is even better.

*Marchette Chute*

## ¡Que llueva!

¡Que llueva! ¡Que llueva!
la virgen de la cueva,
los pajaritos cantan,
las nubes se levantan,

¡Que si! ¡Que no!
¡Que caiga el chaparrón!

## It's Raining!

It's raining! It's raining!
The cavern maiden's calling.
The little birds are singing,
All the clouds are lifting.

Oh yes—Oh no!
Oh! Let the downpour fall.

*a traditional Puerto Rican song*
*English lyrics by Elena Paz*

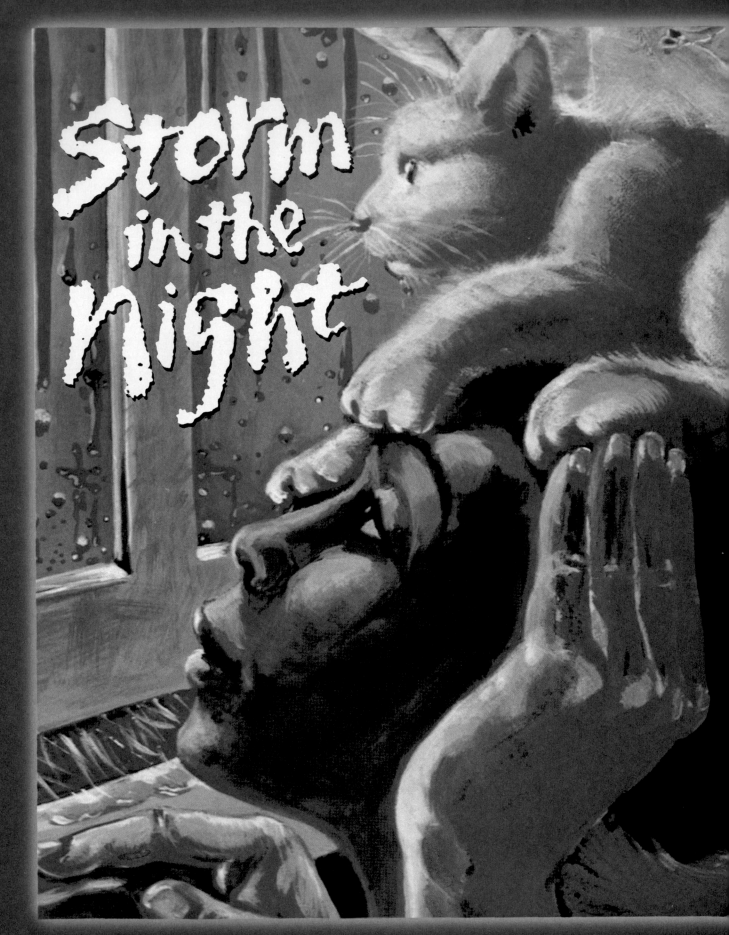

# Storm in the night

by Mary Stolz
illustrated by Pat Cummings

**S**torm in the night.

Thunder like mountains blowing up.

Lightning licking the navy-blue sky.

Rain streaming down the windows, babbling in the downspouts.

And Grandfather? . . . And Thomas? . . . And Ringo, the cat?

They were in the dark. Except for Ringo's shining mandarin eyes and the carrot-colored flames in the wood stove, they were quite in the dark.

"We can't read," said Grandfather.

"We can't look at TV," said Thomas.

"Too early to go to bed," said Grandfather.

Thomas sighed. "What will we do?"

"No help for it," said Grandfather, "I shall have to tell you a tale of when I was a boy."

Thomas smiled in the shadows. It was not easy to believe that Grandfather had once been a boy, but Thomas believed it. Because Grandfather said so, Thomas believed that long, long ago, probably at the beginning of the world, his grandfather had been a boy. As Thomas was a boy now, and always would be.

A grandfather could be a boy, if he went back in his memory far enough; but a boy could not be a grandfather.

Ringo could not grow up to be a kangaroo, and a boy could not grow up to be an old man.

And that, said Thomas to himself, is that.

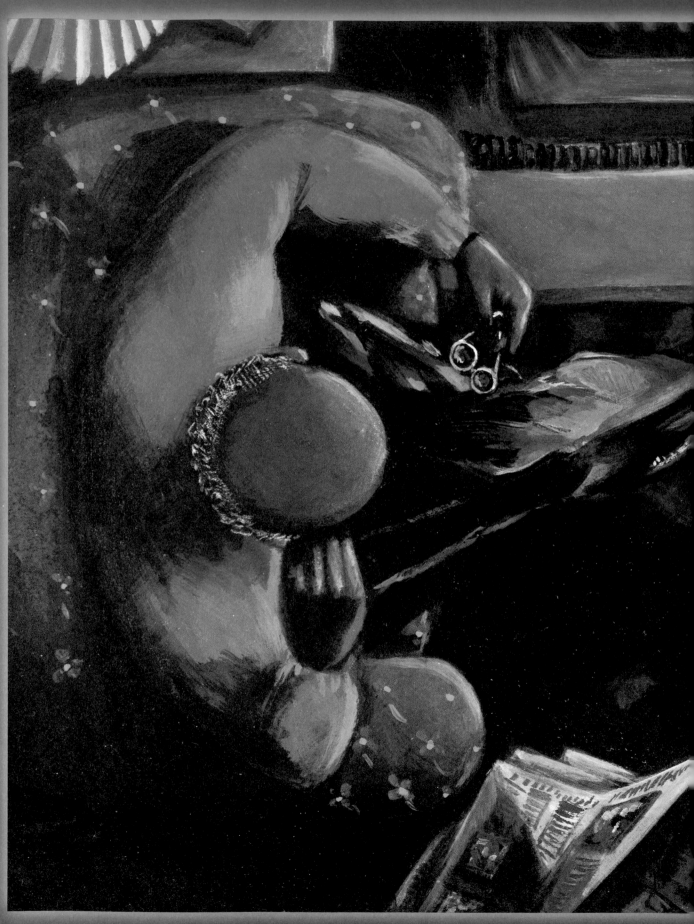

Grandfather was big and bearded.

Thomas had a chin as smooth as a peach.

Grandfather had a voice like a tuba.

Thomas's voice was like a penny whistle.

"I'm thinking," said Thomas.

"Ah," said Grandfather.

"I'm trying to think what you were like when you were my age."

"That's what I was like," said Grandfather.

"What?"

"Like someone your age."

"Did you look like me?"

"Very much like you."

"But you didn't have a beard."

"Not a sign of one."

"You were short, probably."

"Short, certainly."

"And your voice. It was like mine?"

"Exactly."

Thomas sighed. He just could not imagine it. He stopped trying. He tried instead to decide whether to ask for a new story or an old one.

Grandfather knew more stories than a book full of stories. Thomas hadn't heard all of them yet, because he kept asking for repeats.

As he thought about what to ask for, he listened to the sounds of the dark. Grandfather listened too.

In the house a door creaked. A faucet leaked.

Ringo scratched on his post, then on Grandfather's chair. He scratched behind his ear, and they could hear even that.

In the stove the flames made a fluttering noise.

"That's funny," said Thomas. "I can hear better in the dark than I can when the lights are on."

"No doubt because you are just listening," said his grandfather, "and not trying to see and hear at the same time."

That made sense to Thomas, and he went on listening for sounds in the dark.

There were the clocks.

The chiming clock on the mantel struck the hour of eight. *Ping, ping, ping, ping, ping, ping, ping, ping-a-ling.*

The kitchen clock, very excited. *Ticktickticktick-tick*tickety*.*

There were outside sounds for the listening, too.

The bells in the Congregational church rang through the rain. *Bong, bong, bong, bong, bong, bong, bong, BONG!*

Automobile tires swished on the rain-wet streets. Horns honked and hollered. A siren whined in the distance.

"Grandfather," said Thomas, "were there automobiles when you were a boy?"

"Were there *automobiles!*" Grandfather shouted. "How old do you think I am?"

"Well . . ." said Thomas.

"Next thing, you'll be asking if there was electricity when I was your age."

"Oh, Grandfather!" said Thomas, laughing. After a while he said, "Was there?"

"Let's go out on the porch," said Grandfather. "There's too much silliness in here."

By the light of the lightning they made their way to the front door and out on the porch. Ringo, who always followed Thomas, followed him and jumped to the railing.

The rain, driving hard against the back of the house, was scarcely sprinkling here. But it whooped windily through the great beech tree on the lawn, brandishing branches, tearing off twigs. It drenched the bushes, splashed in the birdbath, clattered on the tin roof like a million tacks.

Grandfather and Thomas sat on the swing, creaking back and forth, back and forth, as thunder boomed and lightning stabbed across the sky. Ringo's fur rose, and he turned his head from side to side, his eyes wide and wild in the flashes that lit up the night. The air smelled peppery and gardeny and new.

"That's funny," said Thomas. "I can smell better in the dark, too."

Thomas thought Grandfather answered, but he couldn't hear, as just then a bolt of lightning cracked into the big beech tree. It ripped off a mighty bough, which crashed to the ground. This was too much for Ringo. He leaped onto Thomas's lap and shivered there.

"Poor boy," said Thomas. "He's frightened."

"I had a dog when I was a boy," said Grandfather. "He was so scared of storms that I had to hide under the bed with him when one came. He was afraid even to be frightened alone."

"*I'm* not afraid of *anything*," Thomas said, holding his cat close.

"Not many people can say that," said Grandfather. Then he added, "Well, I suppose anybody could *say* it."

"I'm not afraid of thunderstorms, like Ringo and your dog. What was his name?"

"Melvin."

"That's not a good name for a dog," Thomas said.

"I thought it was," Grandfather said calmly. "He was my dog."

"I like cats," said Thomas. "I want to own a *tiger!*"

"Not while you're living with me," said Grandfather.

"Okay," Thomas said. "Is there a story about Melvin?"

"There is. One very good one."

"Tell it," Thomas commanded. "Please, I mean."

"Well," said Grandfather, "when Melvin and I were pups together, I was just as afraid of storms as he was."

"No!" said Thomas.

"Yes," said Grandfather. "We can't all be brave as tigers."

"I guess not," Thomas agreed.

"So there we were, the two of us, hiding under beds whenever a storm came."

"Think of that . . ." said Thomas.

"That's what I'm doing," said Grandfather. "Anyway, the day came when Melvin was out on some errand of his own, and I was doing my homework, when all at once, with only a rumble of warning . . . *down* came the rain, *down* came the lightning, and all around and everywhere came the thunder."

"Wow," said Thomas. "What did you do?"

"Dove under the bed."

"But what about Melvin?"

"I'm *coming* to that," said Grandfather. "What-about-Melvin is what the story is *about*."

"I see," said Thomas. "This is pretty exciting."

"Well—it was then. Are you going to listen, or keep interrupting?"

"I think I'll listen," said Thomas.

"Good. Where was I?"

"Under the bed."

"So I was. Well, I lay there shivering at every clap of thunder, and

I'm ashamed to say that it was some time before I even remembered that my poor little dog was all by himself out in the storm."

Thomas shook his head in the dark.

"And when I did remember," Grandfather went on, "I had the most awful time making myself wriggle out from under the bed and go looking for my father or my mother—to ask them to go out and find Melvin for me."

"Grandfather!"

"I told you I was afraid. This is a true story you're hearing, so I have to tell the truth."

"Of course," said Thomas, admiring his grandfather for telling a truth like *that.* "Did you find them?"

"I did not. They had gone out someplace for an hour or so, but I'd forgotten. Thomas, fear does strange things to people . . . makes them forget everything but how afraid they are. You wouldn't know about that, of course."

Thomas stroked his cat and said nothing.

"In any case," Grandfather went on, "there I was, alone and afraid in the kitchen, and there was my poor little dog alone and afraid in the storm."

"What did you *do?*" Thomas demanded. "You didn't *leave* him out there, did you, Grandfather?"

"Thomas—I put on my raincoat and opened the kitchen door and stepped out on the back porch just as a flash of lightning

shook the whole sky and a clap of thunder barreled down and a huge man *appeared* out of the darkness, holding Melvin in his arms!"

"Whew!"

"That man was seven feet tall and had a face like a crack in the ice."

"Grandfather! You said you were telling me a true story."

"It's true, because that's how he looked to me. He stood there, scowling at me, and said, 'Son, is this your dog?' and I nodded, because I was too scared to speak. 'If you don't take better care of him, you shouldn't have him at all,' said the terrible man. He pushed Melvin at me and stormed off into the dark."

"Gee," said Thomas. "That wasn't very fair. He didn't know you were frightened too. I mean, Grandfather, how old were you?"

"Just about your age."

"Well, some people my age can get pretty frightened."

"Not you, of course."

Thomas said nothing.

"Later on," Grandfather continued, "I realized that man wasn't seven feet tall, or even terrible. He was worried about the puppy, so he didn't stop to think about me."

"Well, *I* think he should have."

"People don't always do what they should, Thomas."

"What's the end of the story?"

"Oh, just what you'd imagine," Grandfather said carelessly. "Having overcome my fear enough to forget myself and think about Melvin, I wasn't afraid of storms anymore."

"Oh, good," said Thomas.

For a while they were silent. The storm was spent. There were only flickers of lightning, mutterings of thunder, and a little patter of rain.

"When are the lights going to come on?" Thomas asked.

"You know as much as I do," said Grandfather.

"Maybe they won't come on for hours," said Thomas. "Maybe they won't come on until *tomorrow!*"

"Maybe not."

"Maybe they'll *never* come on again, and what will we do then?"

"We'll think of something," said Grandfather.

"Grandfather?"

"Yes, Thomas?"

"What I think . . . I think that maybe if you hadn't been here, and Ringo hadn't been here, and I was all alone in the house and there was a storm and the lights went out and didn't come on again for a long time, like this . . . I think maybe *then* I would be a *little* bit afraid."

"Perfectly natural," said Grandfather.

Thomas sighed.

Grandfather yawned.

Ringo jumped to the porch floor and walked daintily into the garden, shaking his legs.

187

After a while the lights came on.    They turned them off and
went to bed.

# meet Mary Stolz

For Mary Stolz, *Storm in the Night* was a dream come true. "What I wished for was a book that would show at once a peaceful, cozy companionship—the boy, the grandfather, the cat—and an understanding of fear," she explains.

People often ask Stolz the secret to becoming a writer. She replies, "My one-word recipe is READ."

# and Pat Cummings

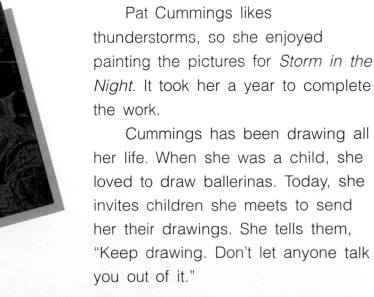

Pat Cummings likes thunderstorms, so she enjoyed painting the pictures for *Storm in the Night*. It took her a year to complete the work.

Cummings has been drawing all her life. When she was a child, she loved to draw ballerinas. Today, she invites children she meets to send her their drawings. She tells them, "Keep drawing. Don't let anyone talk you out of it."

189

WEATHER

IS FULL of the NICEST

SOUNDS!

190

Weather is full
of the nicest sounds:
it sings
and rustles
and pings
and pounds
and hums
and tinkles
and strums
and twangs
and whishes
and sprinkles
and splishes
and bangs
and mumbles
and grumbles
and rumbles
and flashes
and CRASHES.
I wonder
if thunder
frightens a bee,
a mouse in her house,
a bird in a tree,
a bear
or a hare
or a fish in the sea?
Not *me!*

Aileen Fisher

191

# CONTENTS

SOS
SOS
SOS

# Dream Wolf

## by Paul Goble

In the old days the people travelled over the plains. They followed the great herds of buffalo.

Every year when the berries were ripe, they would leave the plains and go up into the hills. They made camp in a valley where the berry bushes grow. Everyone picked great quantities. They mashed the berries into little cakes which they dried in the sun. These they stored in painted bags for the winter.

Tiblo (tee-blow) was too young to play with the older boys. He and his little sister, Tanksi (tawnk-she), had to go berry-picking with their mother and the other women and children.

197

Tiblo was soon tired of picking, and too full to eat any more. When nobody was looking he slipped away with Tanksi to climb the hills.

They climbed up and up among the rocks and cedar trees where bighorn sheep and bears live. Soon they could hardly hear the berry-pickers laughing and calling to each other far below. Tiblo wanted to reach the top. They climbed on.

They never noticed the sun starting to go down behind the hills.

It was getting dark when Tiblo knew they had to go back home. In the twilight every hill and valley looked the same. He did not know which way to go. He called out. . . . Only the echoes answered him.

They wandered on. Tiblo was lost. Darkness closed around them. It grew colder. They were tired and hungry, and Tanksi began to cry.

Speaking of happy things, Tiblo found a small cave among the rocks. They crawled inside to shelter for the night.

The children were tired, and in a little while they fell asleep. Tiblo had a dream.

He dreamed that a wolf with shining eyes entered the cave. In his dream he felt the wolf's hot breath and its rough tongue licking his face. The wolf lay down beside him. His shaggy fur was like a blanket which kept Tiblo and Tanksi warm.

The sun was already shining into the mouth of the cave when Tiblo opened his eyes again.

Tiblo woke up his sister. They crawled out of the cave into the warm sunshine. He took Tanksi by the hand, and they set off walking down the hill.

W hen the children came to a stream, they stopped to drink. Suddenly Tiblo saw that a wolf was sitting on some rocks close by, watching them. At once he remembered his dream.

"O Wolf," Tiblo said, "we are lost. Mother will be crying. Help us to find our way home again."

The wolf panted and smiled. "My children, do not worry. I will help you. Last night you slept in my den. Follow me now, and I will take you home."

The wolf trotted off. He looked back to see that the children were following. From time to time he trotted ahead out of sight, but he always returned.

At last the wolf led them to a hilltop. The children were filled with joy to see their home in the valley below. The wolf sat back on his haunches and smiled. And then he trotted off back toward the hills. The children begged him to come and live with them.

"No," the wolf called back, "I like to wander from place to place with my friends. Listen for me in the evenings! You will hear me calling, and you will know that I never forget you."

People in the camp saw the children coming down the hill. The men jumped on to their horses, and galloped out to bring them home. Everyone was happy that the children were safe.

Tiblo told how the wolf had brought them home. Everyone walked into the hills to thank the wolf. They spread a blanket for him to sit on. They gave him necklaces and other beautiful gifts.

There has been close kinship with the Wolf People for as long as anyone can remember. That is what they say.

The wolves are no longer heard calling
in the evenings at berry-picking time. Hunters
have killed and driven them away with guns
and traps and poisons. People say that the
wolves will return when we, like Tiblo and
Tanksi, have the wolves in our hearts and
dreams again.

# Meet Paul Goble

When Paul Goble was growing up in England, he was interested in Native Americans. To him, their world seemed very different from the "crowded island" where he lived. Later, Goble visited the United States. He stayed with Sioux friends in South Dakota and Crow friends in Montana. When they saw how much he loved their ways, they taught him about their beliefs and folklore. Goble turned what he learned into books. One, *The Girl Who Loved Wild Horses,* received a Caldecott Medal in 1979.

In his books, Paul Goble tries to show what wild animals are really like. He is upset by mistaken ideas about them, such as the notion that "bears are huggable, woodpeckers are destructive, coyotes and tomcats mean." He admires the Native Americans' belief that animals deserve respect because they were on the earth before people.

Paul Goble explains that he has learned many wonderful things from Native American people. He says, "I have simply wanted to express and to share these things which I love so much."

THE GIRL WHO LOVED WILD HORSES
by PAUL GOBLE

OPERATION
14
RESCUE

# OPERATION
from 3-2-1 Contact
## RESC
# SAVING SEA LIFE FROM OIL SPILLS

Sea otters look for danger by standing tall in the water, shading their eyes with their forefeet. But their natural watchfulness couldn't help the otters of Prince William Sound in Alaska one day in 1989.

That's when the oil tanker *Exxon Valdez* hit an underwater reef, causing the worst oil spill ever in U.S. waters. About 11 million gallons gushed into the Alaskan sound, spoiling 304 miles of shoreline.

Whether it's a big spill like the one in Alaska, or smaller ones that have taken place in other parts of the U.S.—a spill can be deadly for the animals who get caught in it. Whales, seals and sea lions seem to get through a spill without much damage because they have blubber to keep warm.

But others, such as sea otters and seabirds, suffer badly. They need help quickly

# UE

by Christina Wilsdon

—or they will freeze to death in the cold ocean water.

"Otters need their thick fur to keep them warm," explains Jim Robinett. He is a marine mammal expert at the Shedd Aquarium in Chicago, Illinois. If an otter's fur gets dirty—or coated with oil—that means danger. The hairs can't help hold warm air next to the body—or keep freezing water out.

"Some birds are so badly coated with oil that it's hard to tell what kinds they are," says Marge Gibson, who runs the Orange County Bird of Prey Rescue Center in Villa Park, California. "You just see this blob with its eyes blinking, and you realize it's alive."

That's when professional animal handlers—and volunteers—get to work. Thanks to these dedicated people, thousands of animals have been saved.

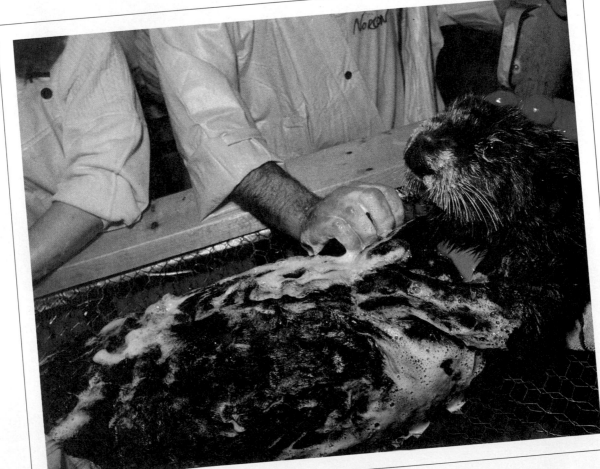

Saving otters starts with scooping them out of the water with long-handled nets. After they are caught, rescuers start to clean the animals. This isn't the easiest job. Big otters can weigh 80 pounds. Their jaws can crush bones. And they move very fast. "We call them 'Slinkies covered with fur,'" says Robinett. "They seem to turn around inside their skins!"

A light dose of anesthesia slows an otter down so that it can be handled, yet be awake. Still, it takes four people to wash one otter.

"Washing" means scrubbing the otter with water and dish soap for 30 to 40 minutes. The otter lies on a screen over a tub made out of half an oil drum. The oily, soapy water drains into the drum. Then the animal is rinsed for 20 to 30 minutes until the soap is gone.

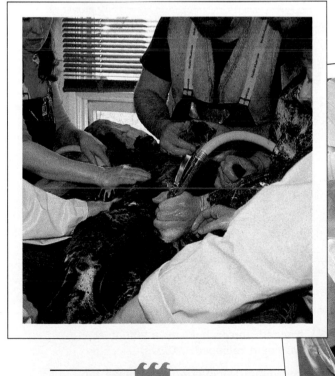

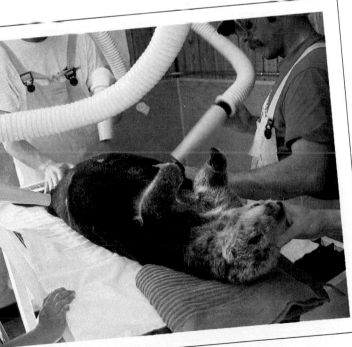

It took almost two hours to wash, rinse, and dry this otter at the Valdez Otter Rescue Center.

215

Oiled otters also have their insides cleaned out. That's because they often swallow oil as they try to lick themselves clean. Oil damages an animal's liver and kidneys. "We tube-feed them a solution that absorbs the poisonous oil that may be in the intestines," explains Robinett. "The solution has tiny bits of charcoal, similar to what people use in a home aquarium."

Next, the otter goes to "intensive care"—an indoor pen filled with soft towels. Even though it survived the oil—as well as the "wash-and-rinse cycle"—the otter is still at risk. When the otter is out of danger, rescuers move it outdoors to a dry pen.

The oil spill left these otter pups orphans. After being rescued, one pup sleeps with a security blanket. *(Left)*

A cleaned pup is held by a volunteer before being released. *(Above)*

It's playtime! Recovering pups have fun in the swimming pool. *(Opposite page)*

Otters also get daily trips to a swimming pool. This way, the otter can groom and clean itself. "Grooming helps produce natural oils, which coat the fur and help create the insulating layer that otters depend on," says Robinett.

Veterinarians, zoo and aquarium keepers keep track of the otter's temperature and food intake. Finally, when it's healthy, the otter is moved into a sea pen where it stays until it's strong enough to be released.

OPERATION RESCUE 14

Seabirds suffer many of the same problems that otters do, but they need different care because they are more delicate.

"A rescued bird is weak," says Nicolette Heaphy, who works at the International Bird Rescue Research Center in Berkeley, California. "It needs fluids, which are tube-fed into its stomach. We place the birds in a pen and don't wash them for 24 hours. They've been through a lot of stress. Washing them in that situation can kill them."

The birds don't get anesthesia or charcoal solution. But they do get a cloth bib to wear around their necks. The bib keeps them from trying to clean, or preen, their feathers. "They preen and preen," says Heaphy. "They just don't understand that the oil isn't removeable."

Seabirds preen because they depend on their feathers to keep them warm and dry. Each feather has many barbs that hook into each other. Plus, the feathers overlap like shingles on a roof. "Many people think a bird is naturally waterproofed," says Heaphy. "Not so. It's the interlocking barbs that create a kind of wetsuit."

**V**olunteers feed a mixture of liquid fish food and vitamins by tube into the mouth of an oiled bird. *(Left)*

**I**f workers miss a spot, the bird could freeze to death in the cold Alaskan waters. *(Right)*

Oil stuck in the barbs prevents the feathers from locking together. Cold water seeps in, soaking the downy feathers that normally hold warm air. It reaches the skin—and soon the bird freezes to death.

Scrubbing a bird would break its feathers. So a team of two washers must use a different method. They place the bird in tub after tub of soapy dish water, pouring cupfuls of water over its body and wings. Then workers use a

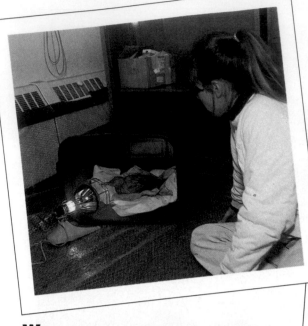

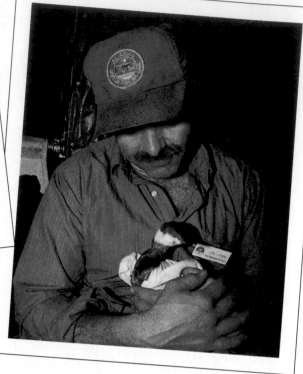

**W**arm air from a heat lamp dries the bird but does not harm its feathers. *(Above)*

**A** rescuer holds a bird that will soon be set free. *(Right)*

soft toothbrush and an electric tooth cleaner to remove oil from the bird's head.

Next, rescuers rinse the bird by forcing jets of water through its feathers. "Detergent is as bad for keeping the feathers waterproofed as oil is," explains Heaphy. So it's important to get all the soap out.

Strangely enough, the bird looks drier the more it is rinsed. This is because its outer feathers start to lock together again. But the downy feathers underneath are still

wet. So the bird is put in a pen and dried with warm air.

"Then the bird is put in a pool to check its waterproofing," explains Heaphy. "Leftover soap or oil will show up as wet spots on the body." Birds that are not waterproofed go back for re-rinsing.

Birds that pass the waterproofing tests are not released right away. They must also be eating well. Their weight and blood are checked, too. When all the medical signs are right, they are banded and set free.

OPERATION 14 RESCUE

The *Valdez* spill left a sad story behind. More than 1,000 otters and more than 30,000 dead seabirds were found. Many others died and were never found. Scientists think that as many as 250,000 birds were killed.

But the rescue workers all speak of the joy they felt when their hard work ended in the release of healthy animals. "The success stories meant a lot to us because so many birds and otters died," biologist James Styers told *3-2-1 Contact*. "Saving any individual animal was worth all the work."

MEET CHRISTINA WILSDON

**C**hristina Wilsdon writes for several children's magazines, including *Electric Company* and *3-2-1 Contact*. About a year after the big 1989 oil spill in Alaska, Wilsdon began to work on an article about that spill. Her desire to write the article came from her lifelong love of animals and her interest in the environment. She hoped to show readers how scientists and volunteers worked together to save the wildlife. She also wanted to help people understand "how precious and beautiful this world is."

# The Toad

I found me a hoptoad
Sitting in the yard.
I tried to watch him,
But watching him was hard.
He hopped in the road
With one big hop,
And I called out, "Toad,
Stop!
Stop!"

"Toad," I yelled,
"Get out of the road.
Here comes a truck
With a mighty heavy load!"

The truck came a-racketing
And roaring on,
And just as I thought:
"There's a good toad gone,"
S l o w l y
The toad hopped onto the lawn.

The toad acted sleepy
As the truck went by,
And while he rested
And blinked a beady eye,
My ears heard a whirring,
And my nose smelled gas,
And up came Willie,
Gaily mowing grass.

The wheels of the power-mower
Never once slowed;
And—suddenly scared—
I shouted, "Toad,
Hurry up.
Hop!
Or you'll get mowed!"

"A mower," I told him,
Trying hard to talk,
"Can grind up a toad
Like a dandelion stalk."
The toad peered over
A bud of white clover
And  s l o w l y
Hopped on the flagstone walk.

That was the second thing
But still not the last.
After a minute
A puppy lolloped past.
I drove off the puppy,
And I scatted a cat,
And I took the toad
To the woods
After that.

I like being helpful,
And I'm no quitter,
But *that* toad needed
A baby sitter.

**Kaye Starbird**

A Friend in Need

**Amigo**
by Byrd
Baylor,
illustrated
by Garth
Williams,
Aladdin,
1989

Can that be Amigo?
Does he read my mind?
Does he know he's the one
That I came to find?

**Jackpot of the Beagle
Brigade**
by Sam and Beryl Epstein,
photographs by
George Ancona,
Macmillan, 1987

Jackpot comes to a cart piled
with suitcases. He starts to
sniff around it.
"Keep your dog away from
my stuff!" the man says.
"He's just
doing his
job," Hal
replies.
Then
Jackpot
sits
down
beside the cart.
This is the signal.

## Meet
## Yoshiko Uchida

Yoshiko Uchida grew up with two cultures. One was the culture that surrounded her home in California. The other consisted of the Japanese customs and traditions of her parents.

Uchida says, "I feel it's so important for Japanese-American—and all Asian-American—children to be aware of their history and culture. . . . At the same time, I write for *all* children, and I try to write about values and feelings that are universal."

Yoshiko Uchida wrote her very first book, *Jimmy Chipmonk and His Friends: A Short Story for Small Children,* at age ten. Animals appear in some of the writings she's done as an adult, too, such as *The Two Foolish Cats* and *The Rooster Who Understood Japanese.*

# The Rooster Who Understood Japanese

by Yoshiko Uchida

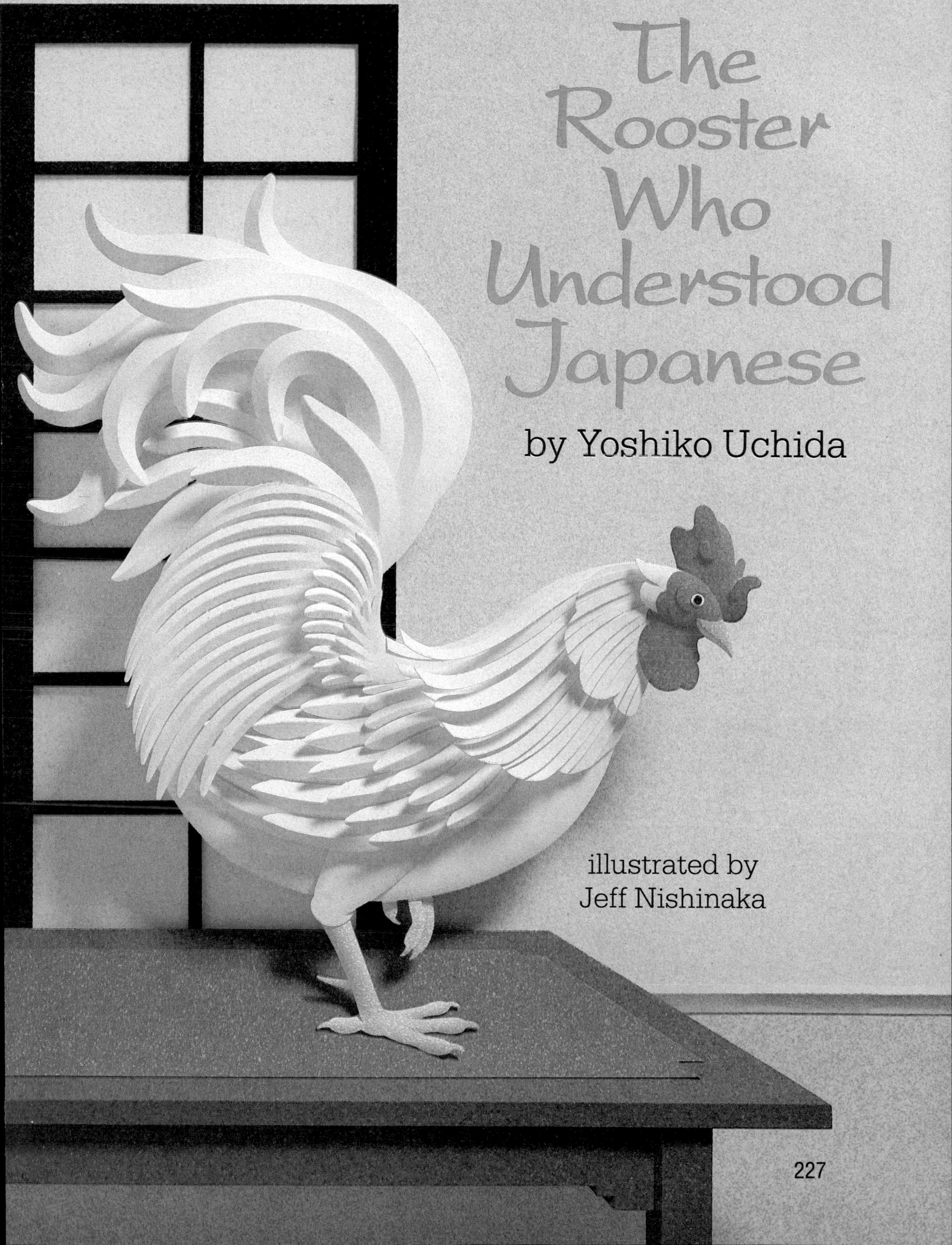

illustrated by
Jeff Nishinaka

"Mrs. K.!" Miyo called. "I'm here!"

Every afternoon when Miyo came home from school, where she was in the third grade, she went to the home of her neighbor, Mrs. Kitamura, whom she called "Mrs. K."

This was because Miyo's mother was a doctor at University Hospital and didn't get home until supper time. Sometimes, she didn't get home even then, and if she didn't, Miyo just stayed on at Mrs. K's.

It was a fine arrangement all around because Mrs. Kitamura was a widow, and she enjoyed Miyo's company. Not that she was lonely. She had a basset hound named Jefferson, a ten-year-old parrot named Hamilton, a coal black cat named Leonardo, and a pet rooster named Mr. Lincoln. She talked to all of them in Japanese. She also talked to the onions and potatoes she'd planted in her front yard instead of a lawn, coaxing them each day to grow plump and delicious.

Miyo stopped next to see Mr. Lincoln. He was strutting about in his pen making rooster-like sounds and looking very intelligent and dignified. Mrs. K. had told Miyo that he understood every word she said to him whether she spoke in English or Japanese.

"Mrs. Kitamura, *doko?*" Miyo said, asking Mr. Lincoln where she was.

He cocked his head, looked at her with his small bright eyes, and uttered a squawking sound.

Miyo shrugged. Maybe Mr. Lincoln did understand Japanese, but it certainly didn't do her any good if she couldn't understand what he said back to her.

"Never mind," she said. "I'll find her." And she hurried toward the brown shingled house covered with ivy that hung over it like droopy hair. The back door was unlatched, and Miyo walked in.

"Mrs. K., I'm here," she called once more.

Immediately a high shrill voice repeated, "Mrs. K., I'm here." It was Hamilton, the parrot, who lived in a big gold cage in Mrs. Kitamura's kitchen.

"Hello, Hamilton," Miyo said.

"Hello, Hamilton," he answered back.

Miyo sniffed as she walked through the kitchen, hoping she might smell chocolate brownies or freshly baked bread. But today there were no nice welcoming smells at all. There was only silence and the smell of floor wax.

Miyo went through the swinging doors into the dining room and found Mrs. K. sitting at the big oval dining room table. She still wore her floppy gardening hat over the pile of gray hair that had been frizzled by a home permanent, and she was doing something Miyo had never seen her do before. She was making herself a cup of ceremonial Japanese tea, whipping up the special powdered green tea in a beautiful tea bowl with a small bamboo whisk.

Miyo knew exactly what Mrs. K. was doing because she had seen a lady in a silk kimono perform the

Japanese tea ceremony at the Buddhist temple just last month.

Somehow Mrs. K. didn't look quite right preparing the tea in her gardening smock and floppy hat, sitting at a table piled high with old newspapers and magazines. Furthermore, she was frowning, and Miyo knew the tea ceremony was supposed to make one feel peaceful and calm.

"*Mah!*" Mrs. K. said, looking startled. "I was so busy with my thoughts, I didn't even hear you come in."

Miyo looked at the pale green froth of tea in the tea bowl, knowing it was strong and bitter. "Is that our afternoon tea?" she asked, trying not to look too disappointed.

"No, no, not yours," Mrs. K. answered quickly. "Just mine. I made it to calm myself." She turned the bowl around carefully and drank it in the proper three and a half sips. "There," she sighed.

"Are you calm now?"

Mrs. K. shook her head. "Not really. Actually, not at all. As a matter of fact, I am most upset."

乾杯

Mrs. Kitamura stood up and started toward the kitchen, and Leonardo appeared from beneath her chair to follow close behind. Miyo thought that was a strange name for a cat, but Mrs. K. had told her he was a very sensitive, creative cat, and she had named him after Leonardo da Vinci.

In fact, all of Mrs. K's pets had very elegant and dignified names which she had chosen after going to a class in American history in order to become an American citizen. She said animals were purer in spirit than most human beings and deserved names that befit their character. "Besides," she had added, "I like to be different."

Mrs. K. certainly was different, all right. She wasn't at all like most of the other elderly ladies who went to the Japanese Buddhist temple.

"It is because I am a free spirit," she had explained to Miyo one day.

Maybe it was because she had lived in America so much longer than the other ladies who had come from Japan. She never did anything she didn't want to do, although she was always careful not to cause anyone any grief.

Miyo wondered now why Mrs. K. was so upset.

Usually she was full of fun, but today she scarcely smiled at Miyo.

"I've been upset since seven o'clock this morning," she explained suddenly.

"Why?" Miyo asked, gratefully accepting a glass of milk and some peanut butter cookies. "Did you get out of the wrong side of bed?"

That was what her mother sometimes asked when Miyo was grumpy. But that wasn't Mrs. K's trouble at all.

"It's not me," she said. "It's my new neighbor, Mr. Wickett. He told me that if Mr. Lincoln didn't stop waking him up by crowing at six in the morning, he was going to report me to the police for disturbing the peace! Can you imagine anything so unfriendly?"

Miyo certainly couldn't. "He's mean," she said.

"What am I going to do?" Mrs. K. asked, as though Miyo were the wise old woman in the Japanese tale who could answer any puzzling question put to her.

"I can't go out and tell Mr. Lincoln he is not to crow anymore. That would be like telling Jefferson not to wag his tail, or telling Leonardo not to groom himself . . ."

"Or telling Hamilton not to mimic us," Miyo said, getting into the spirit of things.

"Exactly," Mrs. K. agreed. "He is only behaving in his natural rooster-like way. And besides," she added, "any respectable old man should be up by six o'clock. You and your mama have never complained."

Miyo didn't say that they were already up at six o'clock anyway. She wondered what she could say to make Mrs. K. feel better, and finally she said, "I'll ask my mother. She'll know what to do."

Miyo's mother usually found a way to solve most problems. She had to because Miyo had no father, and there was no one else in their house to ask. Miyo's father had died long ago and Miyo barely remembered him.

"Don't worry, Mama will think of something," Miyo said as she left Mrs. Kitamura's house.

Mrs. K. nodded. "I hope so," she said dismally. "In the meantime, I must think of something before six o'clock tomorrow morning."

When Miyo got home, Mother was just starting supper. "Hi sweetie," she called. "How was Mrs. K.?"

"She was worried," Miyo answered as she began to set the table. "She's got to make Mr. Lincoln stop crowing."

"Whatever for?"

Miyo quickly told Mother about Mr. Wickett. "He's a mean old man," she said, scowling at the thought of him. "Mr. Lincoln doesn't hurt anybody."

But Mother said, "Well, I can see Mr. Wickett's side too. If I could sleep late, I'm not so sure I'd like having a rooster wake me at six o'clock. Besides," she added, "our town is growing, and we're in the city limits now. Maybe Mrs. K. will just have to give Mr. Lincoln away."

Miyo didn't even want to think of such a thing. "But he's not just any old rooster," she objected.

He certainly wasn't. Mrs. K. had raised him since he was a baby chick, thinking that he was going to become a hen and give her an egg for breakfast every day.

"Besides," she added, "he doesn't crow very loud."

Mother nodded sympathetically. "I know," she said. "Well, maybe we can think of something."

But nobody could. Not mother, not Miyo, nor Mrs. K.

That first night Mrs. K. brought Mr. Lincoln inside the house and stuffed him into a big cardboard carton in her bedroom.

"Poor Mr. Lincoln," she said to Miyo the next day. "He nearly smothered, and I hardly got any sleep at all. He crowed in the morning anyway, but I don't think

Mr. Wickett heard him because so far the police haven't come. But I jump every time my doorbell rings. What on earth are we going to do?" she asked, wrapping Miyo into the bundle of her troubles.

Miyo wished she had an answer, but all she could say was, "Mama and I are both thinking hard."

Mrs. K. had been so worried she had spent the entire day cooking Japanese food to take her mind off her troubles.

"I made two kinds of *osushi* today," she said to Miyo, showing her an enormous platter of flavored rice rolled in sheets of seaweed. She had also cooked slices of fried bean curd and stuffed them with rice so they looked like fox ears. Mrs. K. had been pouring her worries into the fox ears all morning, but like her potatoes and onions, they couldn't tell her what to do.

Mrs. K. gave Miyo a platter of *osushi* when she left. "Take some home for your supper," she said. "Your mama will be glad not to have to cook tonight."

Miyo felt that neither she nor her mother really deserved the *osushi,* for they hadn't come up with a single good idea to help Mrs. K.  But neither had Mr. Kitamura, and he got a small dish of *osushi* too. Mrs. K. had put it in front of his photograph that stood beside the black and gold altar with the small statue of Buddha and the incense and candle.

In fact, ever since he died years ago, Mr. Kitamura always got a small dish of anything good that Mrs. K. made, and Miyo wondered if he came down from the Pure Land in the middle of the night to eat it. Mrs. K. told her, however, that the food was for his spirit, and that it reached him just as her love and thoughts did, in a wonderful way that she couldn't quite explain.

"I do wish we could think of a way to help Mrs. K.," Mother said as they ate Mrs. K's delicious *osushi* and drank steaming cups of tea.

But Mother was so tired at the end of a long day looking after sick babies and children at the hospital that she just couldn't find any good ideas inside her head. She did say, however, that keeping Mr. Lincoln inside a carton in the house was not the answer.

And Mrs. K. certainly found out it wasn't. On the second night she brought him inside, Mr. Lincoln poked his way right out of the carton and walked all over her house. He scratched the floors and pecked at her sofa and got into a fight with Leonardo, the cat. By the time Mrs. K. got to them, there were feathers all over her living room and Leonardo almost had fresh chicken for breakfast.

"I suppose I will have to give Mr. Lincoln away," Mrs. K. murmured sadly. "But I can't give him to just anybody. It has to be someone who will love him and not turn him into fricassee or stew."

Mrs. K. lost three pounds from worrying and said she was becoming a nervous wreck. "If I can't find a new home for Mr. Lincoln, I suppose I will simply have to go to jail," she said, trying to look brave.

Miyo thought and thought until her jaws ached. How in the world could they find just the right person to take Mr. Lincoln? Then, suddenly, she had an idea.

"I know," she said brightly. "I'll put an ad in our class magazine."

Mrs. K. thought about it. "Well," she said slowly, "I suppose it won't do any harm."

What she really meant was that it probably wouldn't do any good either. But Miyo was determined to try. She had to hurry for Mrs. K. had already said several times that she was becoming a nervous wreck, and Miyo certainly didn't want her to stop being the nice, cheerful person she was.

Miyo's class magazine was almost ready to be mimeographed for the month of October. There were several sections, one each for news, feature stories, science, sports, book reviews, poetry, and, finally, a small section for ads. That's where Miyo thought Mr. Lincoln would fit nicely.

Wanted: Nice home for friendly, intelligent, dignified ROOSTER. P.S. He understands Japanese. Please hurry! Urgent! 555-4321

She made her ad very special. She wrote, "WANTED: NICE HOME FOR FRIENDLY, INTELLIGENT, DIGNIFIED ROOSTER. P.S. HE UNDERSTANDS JAPANESE." Then she added, "PLEASE HURRY! URGENT!"

Her teacher, Mrs. Fielding, told her it was a fine ad, and suggested that she include her phone number, so Miyo did. She also drew a picture of Mr. Lincoln beneath her ad, trying to make him look dignified and friendly.

The magazine came out on September 30. That very afternoon, a policeman rang the doorbell of Mrs. K's shaggy ivy-covered house.

"I've a complaint, Ma'am," he said, "about a rooster?" He seemed to think there might have been some mistake.

Mrs. K. sighed. "Come inside, officer," she said. "I've been expecting you." She supposed now she would just have to go

quietly to jail, but first she wanted a cup of tea. "Would you like some tea?" she asked.

Officer McArdle was tired and his feet hurt. "Thank you, Ma'am," he said, and he came inside. He looked all around at Mrs. Kitamura's home, bulging with Japanese things he'd never seen before. There were Japanese dolls dancing inside dusty glass cases. There were scrolls of Japanese paintings hanging on the walls. There was the black and gold Buddhist altar, and spread out all over the dining room table were Japanese books and newspapers. Mrs. K. pushed them aside and put down a tray of tea and cookies.

"*Dozo,*" she said, "please have some tea." She took off her apron and smoothed down her frizzy gray hair. Then she told Officer McArdle all about her troubles with Mr. Lincoln.

He looked sympathetic, but he said, "You're breaking a city law by having a rooster in your yard. You really should be fined, you know."

Mrs. K. was astonished. "Even if I am only barely inside the city limits?"

Officer McArdle nodded. "I'm afraid so. I'll give you two more days to get rid of your rooster. Mr. Wickett says you're disturbing the peace."

Then he thanked her for the tea and cookies and he was gone.

Miyo was proud of the ad in her class magazine, but no one seemed at all interested in Mr. Lincoln. Instead, several people told her how much they liked her feature story about Mr. Botts, the school custodian, who was retiring.

She had written, "Say good-bye to the best custodian Hawthorn School ever had. Mr. Botts is retiring because he is getting tired. At the age of sixty-five, who wouldn't? He and Mrs. Botts are going to Far Creek. He is going to eat a lot and sleep a lot and maybe go fishing. So, so long, Mr. Botts. And good luck!"

Her teacher, Mrs. Fielding, told her it was a fine story.

On her way home, Miyo ran into Mr. Botts himself. He told her it was the first time in his entire life that anyone had written a feature story about him.

When he got home that night, he took off his shoes, sat in his favorite chair, lit a pipe, and read the magazine from cover to cover. At the bottom of page twenty, he saw Miyo's ad about Mr. Lincoln.

"Tami," he said to Mrs. Botts, who happened to be Japanese, "how would you like to have a rooster?"

"A what?"

"A rooster," Mr. Botts repeated. "One that understands Japanese."

Mrs. Botts thought that Mr. Botts had had too much excitement, what with his retirement party at school and all. But he kept right on talking.

"When we move to Far Creek, didn't you say you were going to grow vegetables and raise chickens while I go hunting and fishing?"

Mrs. Botts remembered having said something like that. "Yes, I guess I did."

"Well, if you're going to raise chickens, you'll need a rooster."

"Why, I guess that's so."

"Then we might as well have one that's friendly and dignified," Mr. Botts said, and he went right to the telephone to call Miyo.

"I'll take that rooster you want to find a home for," he said. "My wife, Tami, could talk to it in Japanese too."

Miyo couldn't believe it. Someone had actually read her ad and that someone was Mr. Botts and his wife. They would give Mr. Lincoln a fine home and surely wouldn't turn him into fricassee or stew. At last, she had done something to help Mrs. K. and keep her from becoming a nervous wreck. As soon as she told Mother, she ran right over to tell Mrs. K. the good news.

Mrs. K. was just about to stuff Mr. Lincoln into a wooden crate for the night. When Miyo told her that Mr. Lincoln would have a nice half-Japanese home in Far Creek with Mr. and Mrs. Botts, Mrs. K. gave Miyo such a hug she almost squeezed the breath out of her.

"Hooray! *Banzai!*" Mrs. K. said happily. "Tomorrow we will have a party to celebrate. I shall invite you and your mama, and Mr. and Mrs. Botts." And because Mrs. K. felt so relieved and happy, she even decided to invite Mr. Wickett.

"Even though you are a cross old man," she said to him, "I suppose you were right. A rooster shouldn't live in a small pen at the edge of town. He should live in the country where he'll have some hens to talk to and nobody will care if he crows at the sun."

Mr. Wickett was a little embarrassed to come to Mrs. K's party, but he was too

lonely to say no. He came with a box of chocolate-dipped cherries and said, "I'm sorry I caused such a commotion."

But Mrs. K. told him he needn't be sorry. "Life needs a little stirring up now and then," she admitted. "Besides," she added, "now both Mr. Lincoln and I have found new friends."

Miyo and her mother brought a caramel cake with Mr. Lincoln's initials on it and Mr. and Mrs. Botts brought Mrs. K. a philodendron plant. "Maybe you can talk to it in Japanese now instead of to Mr. Lincoln," Mrs. Botts said, "and don't worry, I'll take good care of him."

"You come on out to visit us and your rooster any time you like," Mr. Botts added.

Miyo's mother promised that one day soon she would drive them all up to Far Creek to see how Mr. Lincoln liked his new home.

When the party was over, Mr. Botts carried Mr. Lincoln in his crate to his station wagon. Mr. Lincoln gave a polite squawk of farewell and Mrs. K. promised she would come visit him soon.

"Good-bye, Mr. Lincoln. Good-bye, Mr. and Mrs. Botts," Miyo called.

From inside Mrs. K's kitchen, Hamilton, the parrot, screeched. "Good-bye, Mr. Lincoln. Good-bye."

Jefferson roused himself from his bed near the stove and came outside to wag his tail at everybody, and Leonardo rubbed up against Mrs. K's legs to remind her that he was still there.

Then Mr. Botts honked his horn and they were gone.

"I hope we'll see each other again soon," Mr. Wickett said to Mrs. K.

"Good night, Mr. Wickett," she answered. "I'm sure we will."

Miyo and her mother thanked Mrs. K. for the nice party and went home, leaving her to say good night to her potatoes and onions before going inside.

"Do you think she'll miss Mr. Lincoln a lot?" Miyo asked.

"She will for a while," Mother answered, "but now she has a new friend and neighbor to talk to."

Miyo nodded. That was true. And even if Mr. Wickett couldn't understand Japanese, at least he could answer back, and maybe that was even better than having an intelligent rooster around.

Miyo was glad everything had turned out so well, and went to bed feeling good inside.

"Good night, Mama," she called softly to
her mother.

"Good night, Miyo," Mother answered as
she tucked her in.

Then, one by one, the lights went out in
all the houses along the street, and soon
only the sounds of the insects filled the dark
night air.

# GOING,

There is bad news and good news in the animal world. The bad news is that many animals are in danger of becoming extinct. The good news is that people are doing things to save some of these animals.

## The Bald Eagle

**THE BAD NEWS** When it was named our national bird in 1782, the bald eagle ranged over all of North America. But until recently it had almost disappeared. Chemicals had polluted the waters in which eagles hunted for fish. People had destroyed many nesting places.

**THE GOOD NEWS** Some of the polluting chemicals were banned. People began to protect some of the eagles' nesting places and to raise eagles and then set them free. Now, more and more bald eagles are being spotted across the nation.

### Red Wolf
Five hundred years ago, thousands of red wolves roamed the southeastern United States. By the early 1990s, only 133 red wolves were left.

### African Elephant
In the early 1980s, scientists counted about 1,500,000 African elephants in zoos and on the African plains. Today, only 400,000 survive.

254

# GOING...

## The Panda Bear

**THE BAD NEWS** In 1980, only a thousand giant pandas were left in the wild. Much of the bamboo on which they depend for food had died or been cut down. People were also killing pandas for their fur. The giant pandas were running out of time.

**THE GOOD NEWS** The remaining bamboo forests are now protected, and new ones are being planted. Laws have been passed to keep people from hunting pandas. The giant panda is still endangered, but now there is hope for the future.

### Golden Lion Tamarin
In 1974, only 174 golden lion tamarins were still alive. Now there are about 500 in zoos and about 200 in Brazilian forests.

### American Bison
In 1850, twenty million bison thundered across the North American plains. By 1889, only 551 were left in the United States. Today, about 30,000 bison live in parks.

# Gone

by David McCord

I've looked behind the shed
And under every bed:
I think he must be dead.

What reason for alarm?
He doesn't know the farm.
I *knew* he'd come to harm!

He was a city one
Who never had begun
To think the city fun.

Now where could he have got?
He doesn't know a lot.
I haven't heard a shot.

That old abandoned well,
I thought. Perhaps he fell?
He didn't. I could tell.

Perhaps he found a scent:
A rabbit. Off he went.
He'll come back home all spent.

Groundhogs, they say, can fight;
And raccoons will at night.
He'd not know one by sight!

I've called and called his name.
I'll never be the same.
I blame myself . . . I blame . . .

All *he* knows is the park;
And now it's growing dark.
A bark? *You hear a bark?*

# TURTLE KNOWS YOUR NAME

*a folk tale from the West Indies*

retold and illustrated by
## Ashley Bryan

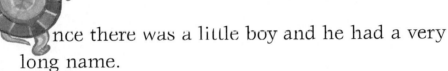

nce there was a little boy and he had a very long name.

His name was UPSILIMANA TUMPALERADO.

It was easy to pronounce, UP-SILI-MANA TUM-PA-LERADO, but it was hard to remember.

His grandmother raised him in her village by the sea.

She taught him to walk. She taught him to talk. But teaching him to walk and to talk wasn't the same as teaching him to say his name, uh-uh!

That took time, and Granny took her time. She said his name to him slowly:

"UP-SILI-MANA TUM-PA-LERADO."

"UPALA TUMPALO!" said the grandson.

"Uh-uh!" said Granny, shaking her head from side to side. "Uh-uh, uh-uh!"

She didn't give up, though.

"Turtle takes his time," she said. "I take mine, and you take your time, too."

And he did. Then one day he said it:

"UPSILIMANA TUMPALERADO!"

"Uh-huh!" cried the grandmother.

She was so happy, she hugged him once, she kissed him twice, she swung him around, wheee, three times! She shook his hand, then took his hand, and they ran down to the sandy beach.

"Here's where we dance your name dance," said Granny. "Sing your name, loud and clear. Sing it to me. Sing it to the sea!"

Granny clapped as they danced. Her grandson sang:

> *"UPSILIMANA TUMPALERADO,*
> *That's my name.*
> *I took my time to learn it,*
> *Won't you do the same?"*

Turtle, who lived nearby, heard the singing and swam closer. The villagers always came to the shore to sing and dance their children's names. Turtle loved to gather names, and he never missed a name dance. Turtle was older than anyone could tell. He even remembered Granny's name dance when Granny, as a little girl, danced with her granny on the shore. Turtle raised his head above the water and listened.

"UPSILIMANA TUMPALERADO, that's my name," sang the boy again and again.

"A long name," said Turtle. "But a good song name to dance to. I think I've got it."

Turtle flipped and dove to the bottom of the sea. In his coral home, Turtle smoothed a space and spelled the name with shells. He blinked and said:

"UPSILIMANA TUMPALERADO, uh-huh! I know it well."

Now that her grandson knew it well, too, Granny let him go out alone to play in the village. Each time he set out to play, she'd say:

"UPSILIMANA TUMPALERADO, teach your name to your playmates and do your best. Remember, your name is long, but it's not the longest."

UPSILIMANA TUMPALERADO always had a good time playing with the village children. He learned their names quickly: Zamba, Mogans, Dandoo, Brashee . . . and he remembered them. He taught them his name, too. But no one ever remembered it.

"Ho, Long Name!" they'd call. "Your turn to hide the stick."

"My name is not Long Name," he'd say. "My name is UPSILIMANA TUMPALERADO."

"Uh-huh," they'd say. "But it's still your turn, Long Name."

His name *was* always the longest. What, then, did Granny mean when she'd say, "Your name is long, but it's not the longest"?

One morning UPSILIMANA TUMPALERADO said, "Granny, I'm not going to be called Long Name today. I'm going to play with the animals."

"Don't be late for dinner," said Granny. "I'm cooking fungi."

"Fungi!" exclaimed the boy.

"Uh-huh!" said Granny. "If you're late, I might be tempted to eat all the fungi myself."

"Uh-uh!" said the boy. "I won't be late! You'll see. Bye, Granny. Twee-twaa-twee."

Off he went, whistling twee-twaa-twee, twee-twaa-twee.

He came to a field and saw a donkey rubbing its hide against a tree. The boy sang:

> *"Donkey, hee, donkey, oh!*
> *My name is UPSILIMANA TUMPALERADO.*
> *Shall I call it out once more?"*

The donkey brayed, "Haw, hee-haw," and rubbed its hide just as before.

"Well, twee-twaa-twee," whistled the boy, and he ran across the field. He clambered up on the rocks bordering the field. There he met a goat bounding from stone to stone. The boy sang:

*"Goat, hah, goat, oh!*
*My name is UPSILIMANA TUMPALERADO.*
*Say it loud. Say it clear."*

The goat bleated, "Bleah, bleah-bleah," and leaped
as if it didn't care.

"Well, twee-twaa-twee," whistled the boy. He
jumped from the rocks into the pasture near the
seashore. There he saw a cow. The boy sang:

*"Cow, ho, cow, oh!*
*My name is UPSILIMANA TUMPALERADO.*
*Say it, and I'll dance for you."*

The cow lowed, "Moo, moo-moo," then mooed
once more and stopped to chew.

"Well, twee-twaa-twee," whistled the boy. He spun
around swiftly and bumped into a pig.

"Oh, pardon, pig," he said. "My name is . . ." and
he stopped short.

"Uh-uh! I won't tell you my name. You'll do the
same as the others."

He ran past pig in the pasture, past pawpaw and palm trees till he came to the beach.

He splashed in the sea, whistling, "Twee-twaa-twee."

Turtle heard the splashing. He swam up to the boy and said:

> "UPSILIMANA TUMPALERADO,
> I'm so glad you came.
> UPSILIMANA TUMPALERADO,
> Turtle knows your name."

The boy slapped the water for joy, splish-splash, splish-splash!

"Turtle, oh, Turtle," he cried. "How did you know that my name is UPSILIMANA TUMPALERADO?"

Turtle didn't stay to play or answer questions. He dove under the waves and disappeared.

The boy called and called till his stomach ached, but Turtle did not return.

"I've yelled myself hoarse, hollow, and hungry," he said to himself. "The fungi, oh, the fungi!"

He ran as fast as he could go. He ran past pawpaw and palm trees, past pig in the pasture, past cow who gazed, grazed, and mooed, past goat bounding high over the rocks, bleah-bleah, past donkey in the field, hee-haw, hee-haw. He ran into his house, crying:

"Granny! Granny! Please, I'm hungry. The fungi, the fungi!"

With her large wooden spoon, Granny was turning the cornmeal in the pot. She smiled at her grandson as she ladled some into a buttered bowl and shook it till it was round as a grapefruit. She rolled it onto her grandson's plate of fish.

"Thank you, Granny. Fungi rolled in a bowl till it's round as a ball and as yellow as gold is the best of all."

"Sing it!" said Granny. She hummed as she shook a bowl of fungi for herself:

> *"Fungi rolled in a bowl*
> *Till it's round as a ball*
> *And as yellow as gold*
> *Is the best of all."*

They finished eating the fungi and fish. Then Granny set a plate of bread pudding and a sweet-potato pie on the table.

"He who asks, don't get. He who don't ask, don't want," said Granny.

Granny always said that before offering dessert. She'd laugh as she watched the puzzled look on her grandson's face. Then she'd offer him a way out.

"Tell me a proverb," she'd say, "and I'll give you dessert."

"A proverb? No problem!" UPSILIMANA TUMPALERADO would say. He had learned lots of proverbs.

He'd answer with: "A man can't grow taller than his head" or "You'll never catch a black cat at night." His favorite was "If a baboon wants to whistle, don't stop him."

But this time, Granny didn't ask for a proverb.

Instead she said, "Tell me my name, UPSILIMANA TUMPALERADO."

"Oh, Granny, that's easier than a proverb," said the boy. "Your name is Granny!"

He laughed and passed his plate.

"Uh-uh," said Granny. "There are grannies all over the village. Every granny has a name. Tell me mine, or no dessert."

Granny took a bite of her bread pudding. UPSILIMANA TUMPALERADO looked at Granny. She licked her lips and rolled her eyes. He looked longingly at the dessert.

"I will find out your real name, Granny," he said. "Then I will have dessert, too."

UPSILIMANA TUMPALERADO jumped up from the table and ran off to the village. He stopped the villagers and asked:

> "Do you know my granny's name?
> Will you tell it to me plain?
> I won't get bread pudding
> Or sweet-potato pie
> Until I tell her real name to her;
> Saying 'Granny' just won't do her."

The villagers circled him and sang:

> "Grass, plants, bees, bells,
> Sky, birds, seas, shells,
> Guava, plantain, mango trees—
> Call them anything you please.
> They will always be the same
> 'Cause Granny is your granny's name."

The villagers danced as they sang the song over and over. Drummers picked up the beat. For a while, UPSILIMANA TUMPALERADO forgot his question and danced quick steps to match the best of the dancers. Then he remembered.

"This won't get me dessert," he said to himself.

He could hear the villagers still chanting, "Granny is your granny's name," as he hurried away to the animals.

He ran to the donkey, haw, hee-haw. Donkey wouldn't help him, didn't want to. Goat and cow were just the same, wouldn't help him with the name, bleah-bleah, moo-moo.

Perhaps Turtle would help. Turtle knew his name. Turtle had said his name before. He kept on running till he reached the shore.

He called till Turtle swam up from his coral home at the bottom of the sea. Then the boy sang:

> *"Turtle, tell me Granny's name.*
> *Will you tell it to me plain?*
> *I won't get bread pudding*
> *Or sweet-potato pie*
> *Until I tell her real name to her;*
> *Saying 'Granny' just won't do her."*

Turtle listened to the sweet, sad song. Then Turtle sang:

> *"UPSILIMANA TUMPALERADO,*
> *Turtle knows your name.*
> *Gathering names is what I do.*
> *I know Granny's real name, too."*

273

"Oh, teach me, Turtle, teach me!" cried the boy.

"First, promise not to tell who told you," said Turtle.

The boy promised and Turtle taught him his granny's name.

"Uh-huh! So that's why Granny always says to me, 'Your name is long, but it's not the longest.'"

He thanked Turtle and ran home.

"Dessert, please, dessert!" cried the boy as he ran into the room.

"Well, UPSILIMANA TUMPALERADO, first tell me my real name."

"Your name is MAPASEEDO JACKALINDY EYE PIE TACKARINDY!"

"Why, UPSILIMANA TUMPALERADO, that's right, uh-huh!"

She served her grandson a large square of bread pudding.

"Tell me, UPSILIMANA TUMPALERADO, who told you my name?"

"Oh, MAPASEEDO JACKALINDY EYE PIE TACKARINDY, I can't tell you."

"Why can't you tell me, UPSILIMANA TUMPALERADO?"

"I promised not to, MAPASEEDO JACKALINDY EYE PIE TACKARINDY."

"Well, then, UPSILIMANA TUMPALERADO, I'll find out for myself."

Granny put on her large straw hat and went into the village. She stopped in the marketplace and said to the villagers:

*"My grandson came*
*And asked my name.*
*Did you tell it?*
*Who can spell it?"*

The villagers clapped and sang:

*"Long Name came*
*And asked your name.*
*So we told him, and it's true,*
*Granny is our name for you."*

"That's not the name my grandson told me," said Granny, and off she went.

Granny's search for an answer took her across the field, over the rocks, through the pasture. She asked the same question of all the animals she met along the way. Donkey bawled, "Haw, hee-haw." Goat bleated, "Bleah, bleah-bleah." Cow answered, "Moo, moo-moo." None of that would do.

At last Granny came to the beach. Turtle was sunning himself on the sand, out of reach of the waves. She sat down beside him and asked:

*"Turtle, did you teach my name?*
*My grandson says it well.*
*Were you the one who made him promise*
*Not to tell?"*

Turtle answered:

*"Yes, I taught your grandson*
*To say your name.*
*I thought it was the thing to do.*
*And now, I'll tell it to you, too.*
*It's MAPASEEDO JACKALINDY EYE PIE*
    *TACKARINDY."*

    Granny leaped up and spun with the news.
    "How did you remember my long, long name
from so long ago?" asked Granny.
    Turtle answered:

*"I learn names from the beach name dances.*
*I remember them well, because I take no chances.*
*I swim up and listen, though you don't see me.*
*Then I spell your names in shells at the bottom of*
    *the sea."*

    Turtle rose up on his short legs and waddled to the
water. With a swish, swoosh, he slipped into the sea.
    Granny waved as Turtle swam out. He dove and
disappeared as Granny sang:

*"Turtle knows your name, uh-huh!*
*Turtle knows your name."*

    When Granny reached home, her grandson stood
at the door with an empty plate. He'd eaten all the
bread pudding.
    "Oh, MAPASEEDO JACKALINDY EYE PIE
TACKARINDY," he said, "now for some sweet-potato pie."

"Aha, UPSILIMANA TUMPALERADO," said MAPASEEDO JACKALINDY EYE PIE TACKARINDY, "I know who knows our names."

They smiled at each other and called out together:

"Turtle knows your name!"

Then MAPASEEDO JACKALINDY EYE PIE TACKARINDY hugged UPSILIMANA TUMPALERADO and cut two slices of sweet-potato pie.

"Thank you, MAPASEEDO JACKALINDY EYE PIE TACKARINDY," said UPSILIMANA TUMPALERADO. "I love your pudding. I love your sweet-potato pie."

"Well, good, UPSILIMANA TUMPALERADO," said MAPASEEDO JACKALINDY EYE PIE TACKARINDY. "You can thank Turtle for dessert."

"Uh-huh, MAPASEEDO JACKA . . ."

But before he could finish saying her name, Granny clapped her hand over her grandson's mouth.

"Listen," she said, "promise not to tell anyone else my name. And from now on, just call me 'Granny' and nothing more. Call me 'Granny,' the way you did before."

UPSILIMANA TUMPALERADO shook his head, and Granny took her hand from his mouth.

"Uh-huh, Granny!" he said.

"And furthermore," said Granny, "from now on, I'm going to call you 'Son.'"

They burst out laughing and finished the pie.

"Mmm . . . I love you, Granny!"

"Mmmm . . . mmm . . . I love you, Son!"

# Meet Ashley

Ashley Bryan learned at an early age to use his drawing talent. In kindergarten, he created his first books, which were *A-B-C* and counting books.

Bryan's childhood was filled with music. Sweet sounds came from his father's saxophone, guitar, and banjo. His mother sang often, and so did the many birds in the family's apartment.

The artist's drawings of animals and people dance across the pages of the African and Caribbean folk tales he retells. Bryan splashes *Turtle Knows Your Name* with colorful paintings. In other books, he uses

Woodcut illustration from
**Lion and the Ostrich Chicks**

282

*Bryan*

Woodcut illustration from
**Beat the Story Drum, Pum-Pum**

bold woodcuts or lively line drawings. Bryan's
storytelling and drawings come both from his
African heritage and from everyday life.
He says about his writing, "I play with
sounds and I encourage others to read
my stories aloud."

Perhaps the turtle in *Turtle Knows
Your Name* also knows Ashley Bryan's
name. Of course, many people do
know and respect the name of
Ashley Bryan. In fact, some
of these people gave him the
Coretta Scott King Award for his book
*Beat the Story Drum, Pum-Pum.*

Line drawing from
**The Dancing Granny**

Woodcut illustration from
**Walk Together Children**

# HURT
# NO
# LIVING
# THING

Hurt no living thing,

Ladybird nor butterfly,

Nor moth with dusty wing,

Nor cricket chirping cheerily,

Nor grasshopper, so light of leap,

Nor dancing gnat,

Nor beetle fat,

Nor harmless worms that creep.

Christina Rossetti

*Tropical Forest with Monkeys*
by Henri Rousseau

# INFORMATION ILLUSTRATED

## YOUR GUIDE TO A WORLD OF INFORMATION — WITH EXAMPLES RELATED TO THE THEMES YOU ARE EXPLORING!

# Contents

287

# Charts and Tables

## SOME OF OUR NATIONAL PARKS

### THE UNITED STATES HAS 50 NATIONAL PARKS.

| NAME | LOCATION | YEAR(S) ESTABLISHED | RANK IN SIZE | SPECIAL FEATURES |
|---|---|---|---|---|
| Badlands | South Dakota | 1929–1978 | 25 | bison, bighorn sheep, antelope, fossil animals 40 million years old |
| Channel Islands | California | 1938–1980 | 24 | sea lion breeding grounds, nesting sea birds, unusual plants |
| Everglades | Florida | 1934 | 9 | largest remaining subtropical wilderness in continental U.S. |
| Grand Canyon | Arizona | 1908–1919 | 10 | most spectacular part of Colorado River canyon |
| Great Smoky Mountains | North Carolina and Tennessee | 1926–1934 | 17 | largest mountain range in eastern U.S., magnificent forests |
| Kenai Fjords | Alaska | 1978–1980 | 15 | mountain goats, marine mammals, bird life, large icecap |
| Olympic | Washington | 1909–1938 | 12 | mountain wilderness with finest remaining rain forest of Pacific Northwest |
| Redwood | California | 1968 | 34 | Pacific coastline, groves of ancient redwoods, world's tallest trees |
| Samoa | American Samoa | 1988 | 49 | tropical rain forest |
| Yellowstone | Idaho, Wyoming, Montana | 1872 | 7 | geysers, hot springs, canyons waterfalls, grizzly bear, moose, bison |

# SOME RARE ANIMALS

| NAME OF ANIMAL (KIND) | NUMBER IN WILD (ESTIMATED) | NUMBER IN ZOOS | YOUNG BORN IN ZOOS (1988) |
| --- | --- | --- | --- |
| Cougar (Florida) | 30 | 2 | 0 |
| Elephant (Asian) | X | 238 | 1 |
| Gorilla (mountain) | 400 | 1 | X |
| Leopard (snow) | 1,000 | 292 | 27 |
| Lion (Asiatic) | 250 | 196 | 0 |
| Rhinoceros (black) | 3,500 | 130 | 5 |
| Anteater | X | 107 | 4 |
| Bear (polar) | 10,000 | 200 | 6 |
| Jaguar | X | 202 | 12 |
| Panda (giant) | 1,000 | 17 | 0 |
| Condor (California) | 0 | 68 | 0 |
| Parrot (golden-shouldered) | 250 | 22 | 9 |
| Boa (Puerto Rican) | X | 63 | 14 |
| Crocodile (Cuban) | 1,000 | 83 | 1 |
| Frog (Goliath) | X | 3 | X |

x = not known

# A WEATHER STATION

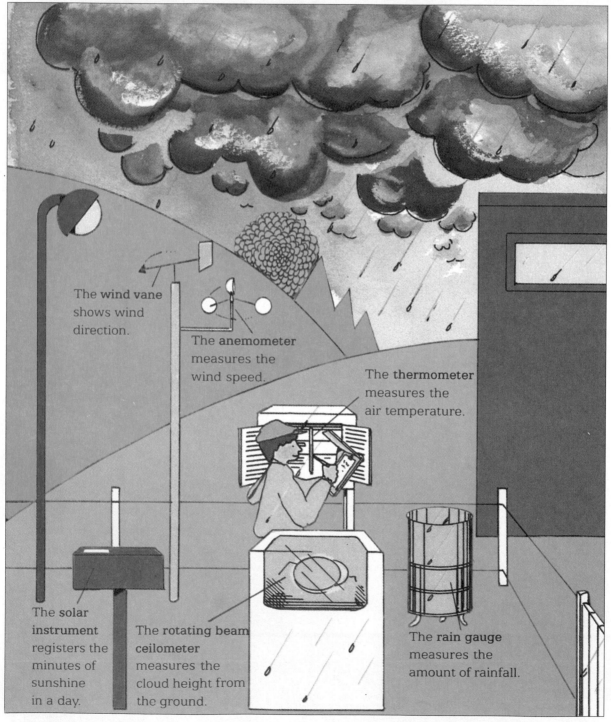

The **wind vane** shows wind direction.

The **anemometer** measures the wind speed.

The **thermometer** measures the air temperature.

The **solar instrument** registers the minutes of sunshine in a day.

The **rotating beam ceilometer** measures the cloud height from the ground.

The **rain gauge** measures the amount of rainfall.

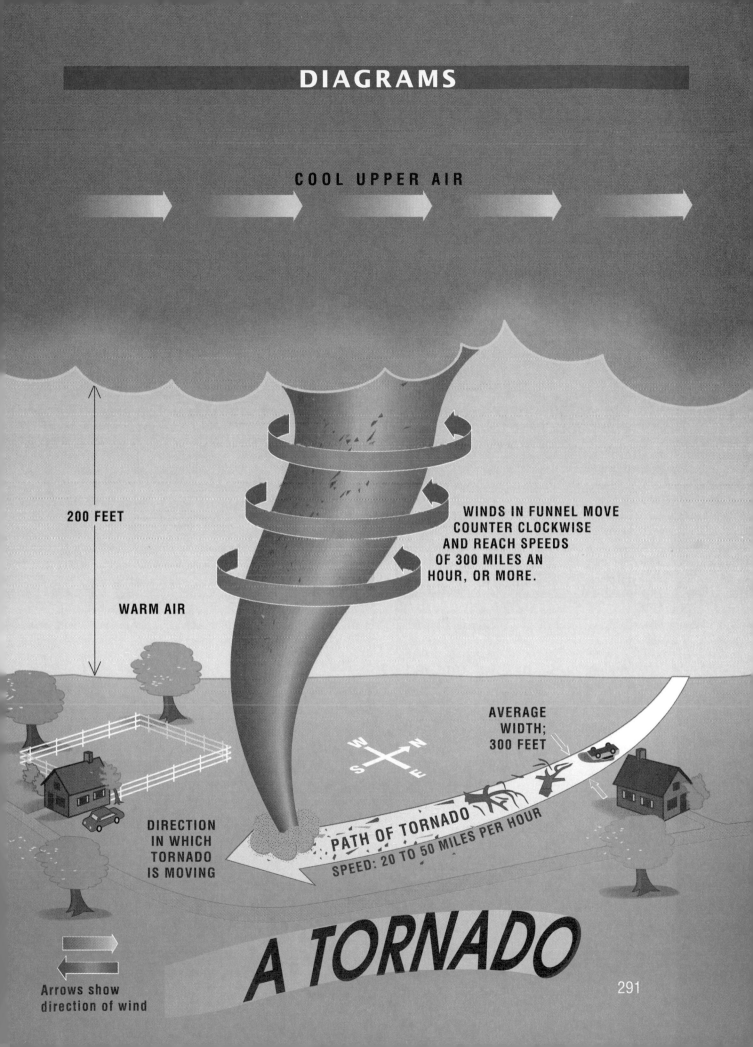

COOL UPPER AIR

200 FEET

WARM AIR

WINDS IN FUNNEL MOVE
COUNTER CLOCKWISE
AND REACH SPEEDS
OF 300 MILES AN
HOUR, OR MORE.

AVERAGE
WIDTH;
300 FEET

DIRECTION
IN WHICH
TORNADO
IS MOVING

PATH OF TORNADO
SPEED: 20 TO 50 MILES PER HOUR

# A TORNADO

Arrows show
direction of wind

# Forms and Applications

## SAN BARTEL ANNUAL DOG SHOW ENTRY FORM

Please fill out this form. It will help us know more about you and your dog. Please print clearly.

| Bridgit | Dalmatian | 2 years, 4 months |
|---|---|---|
| Dog's name | Breed | Dog's age (years, months) |

| Niki | Sarah | May 28, 1985 |
|---|---|---|
| Owner's last name | First name | Date of Birth (month, day, year) |

4364 Claremont St.    Redstone    NM    10040
Street address                      City        State    Zip code

555-8324
Home telephone number

**Write "yes" or "no" on the line.**
1. Is this the first time you have entered a dog in a show? ____yes____
2. Has your dog received the required shots? ____yes____
3. Did you train your dog yourself? ____no____

_____

If you are under 16 years of age, please have your parent or guardian fill out this part of the form.
I give my child ___Sarah Niki___ permission to enter a dog in the San Bartel Dog Show.

_Jeannette Niki_                    _July 15, 1993_
Signature of parent or guardian                 Date

## THE NEWTON PUBLIC LIBRARY

### APPLICATION
### FOR A CHILDREN'S LIBRARY CARD

Please read the statement, sign your name on the line, and answer the following questions.

I will obey the rules of the Newton Public Library and notify the library if I change my address or lose my card.

First Name _Roger_ Last Name _Montana_

Date _Sept. 3, 1993_

1. When is your birthday? _April 17_
2. How old are you? _8_
3. In what language do you like to read, if other than English? _none_
4. What is the name of your school? _Porter School_
5. What grade are you in? _third_

Please print clearly. Enter only one letter or number in each box.

Last Name: | M | O | N | T | A | N | A | | | | | |

First Name: | R | O | G | E | R | | | | | | | |

Middle Initial: | S |

Street Address: | 1 | 7 | 5 | | B | E | E | C | H | | | |

City: | N | E | W | T | O | N | | | | | | |

State: | M | D |

Zip Code: | 0 | 0 | 0 | 0 | 0 |

Phone Number: | 5 | 5 | 5 | – | 4 | 7 | 3 | 9 |

Parent or Guardian–Last Name: | M | O | N | T | A | N | A | | | | | |

Parent or Guardian–First Name: | G | L | O | R | I | A | | | | | | |

Library Card No.: | 7 | 7 | 2 | 8 | 3 |

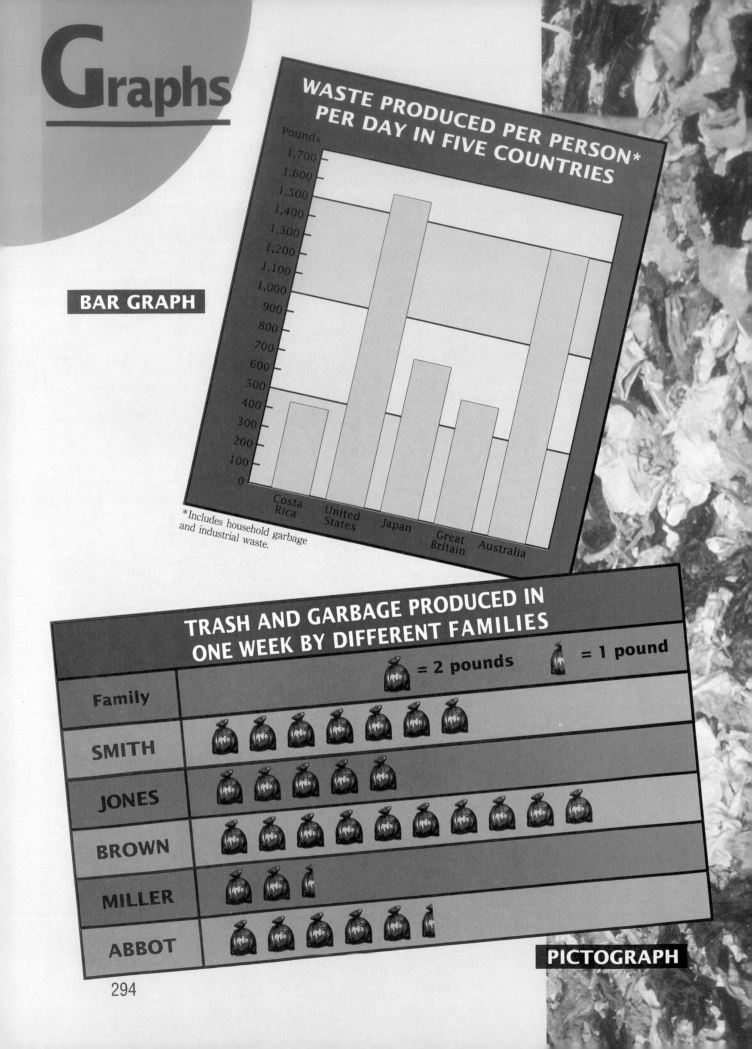

# Graphs

**BAR GRAPH**

## WASTE PRODUCED PER PERSON* PER DAY IN FIVE COUNTRIES

Pounds
1,700
1,600
1,500
1,400
1,300
1,200
1,100
1,000
900
800
700
600
500
400
300
200
100
0

Costa Rica    United States    Japan    Great Britain    Australia

*Includes household garbage and industrial waste.

## TRASH AND GARBAGE PRODUCED IN ONE WEEK BY DIFFERENT FAMILIES

= 2 pounds    = 1 pound

| Family | |
|---|---|
| SMITH | |
| JONES | |
| BROWN | |
| MILLER | |
| ABBOT | |

**PICTOGRAPH**

# WHAT HAPPENS TO WASTE

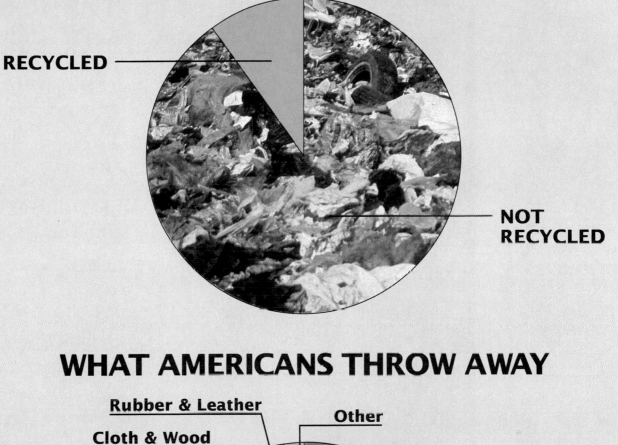

RECYCLED

NOT
RECYCLED

# WHAT AMERICANS THROW AWAY

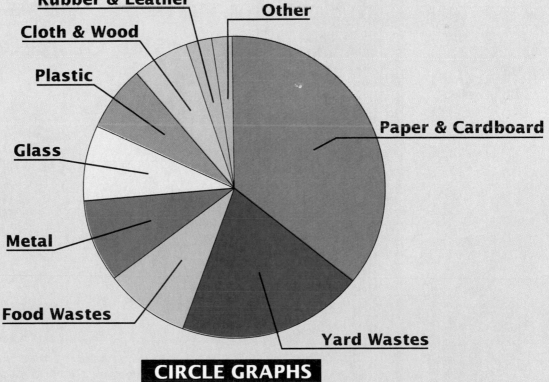

Rubber & Leather

Cloth & Wood

Other

Plastic

Paper & Cardboard

Glass

Metal

Food Wastes

Yard Wastes

**CIRCLE GRAPHS**

295

# Maps

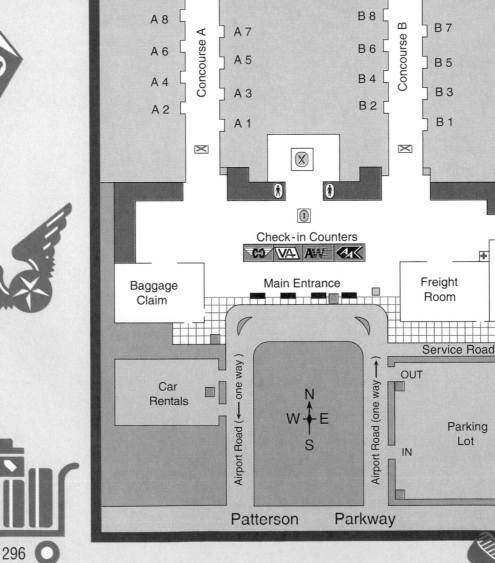

# CITY AIRPORT

## Key

| ■ Shuttle Bus Stop | ① Information | ▢ Lost and Found | **Airlines** |
| ▬ Automatic Door | ⊗ Restaurant | **Restrooms** | ⌁ Continental Carriers |
| ▢ Mailbox | ⊠ Security Check | ♂ Men | VA Vacation Airlines |
| ✚ First Aid Station | ▨ Shops | ♀ Women | AW Air West |
| | | | 4K Arrow Air |

A 10

A 11     A 9

A 8

A 6     A 7

A 4     A 5

A 2     A 3

A 1

Concourse A

B 10

B 11     B 9

B 8

B 6     B 7

B 4     B 5

B 2     B 3

B 1

Concourse B

⊗

♂     ♀

① 

Control Tower

Check-in Counters

⌁ VA AW 4K

✚

Weather Station

Baggage Claim

Main Entrance

Freight Room

Car Rentals

Airport Road ( ← one way )

N
W ✦ E
S

Airport Road (one way →)

Service Road

OUT

Parking Lot

IN

Patterson    Parkway

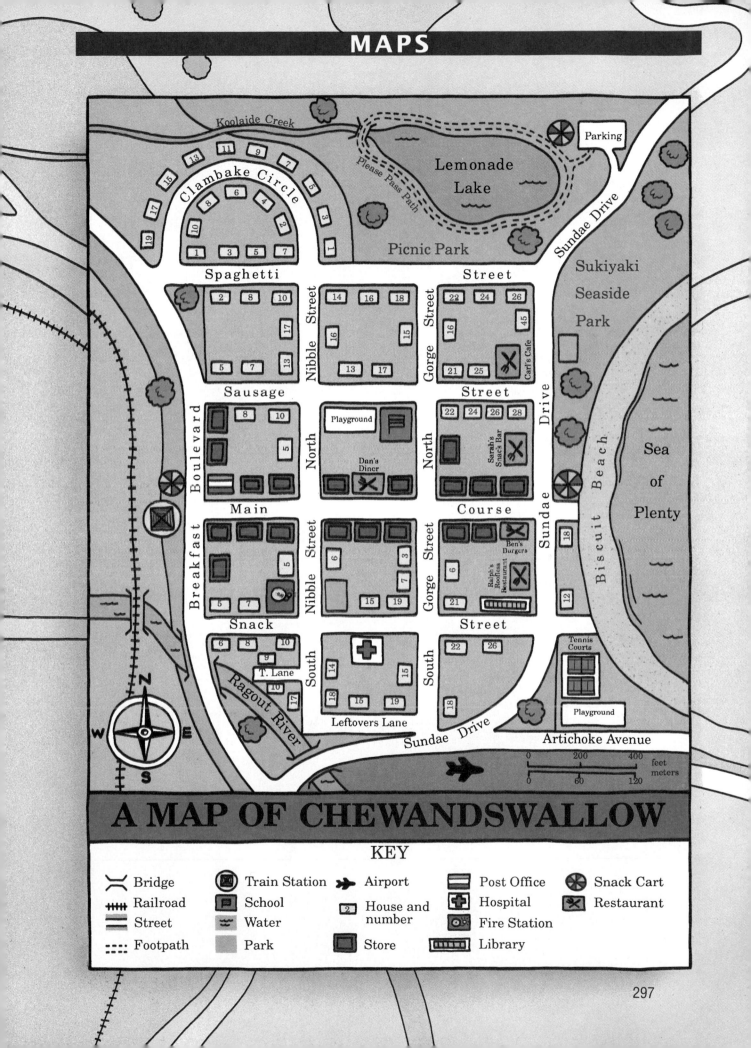

# A MAP OF CHEWANDSWALLOW

## KEY

| | | |
|---|---|---|
| ⋈ Bridge | ⊡ Train Station | ✈ Airport |
| ┼┼┼┼ Railroad | ⊞ School | ▣ House and number |
| ▤ Street | ≋ Water | |
| ⋯ Footpath | ▨ Park | ▢ Store |

| | |
|---|---|
| ▤ Post Office | ⊛ Snack Cart |
| ✚ Hospital | ✖ Restaurant |
| ▣ Fire Station | |
| ▦ Library | |

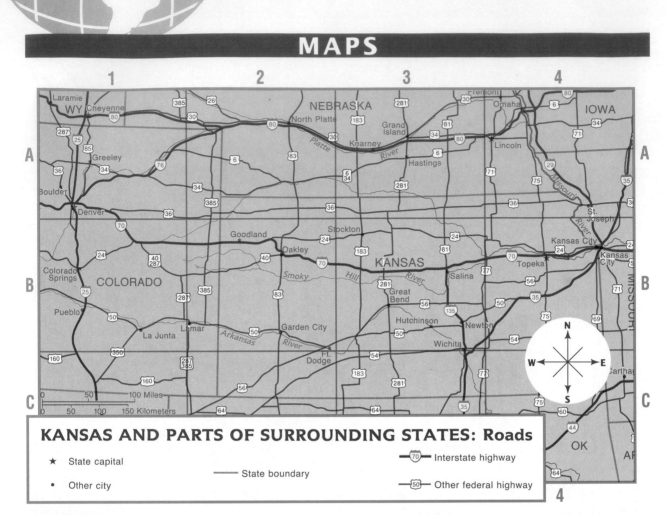

**KANSAS AND PARTS OF SURROUNDING STATES: Roads**

★  State capital

•  Other city

——— State boundary

🛣70 ——— Interstate highway

🛣50 ——— Other federal highway

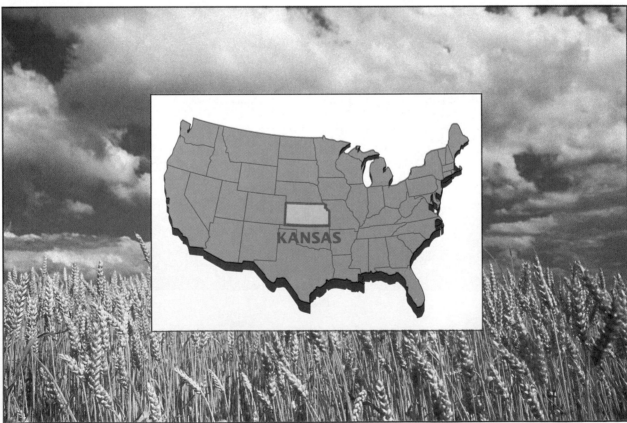

298

# WEATHER MAP: UNITED STATES

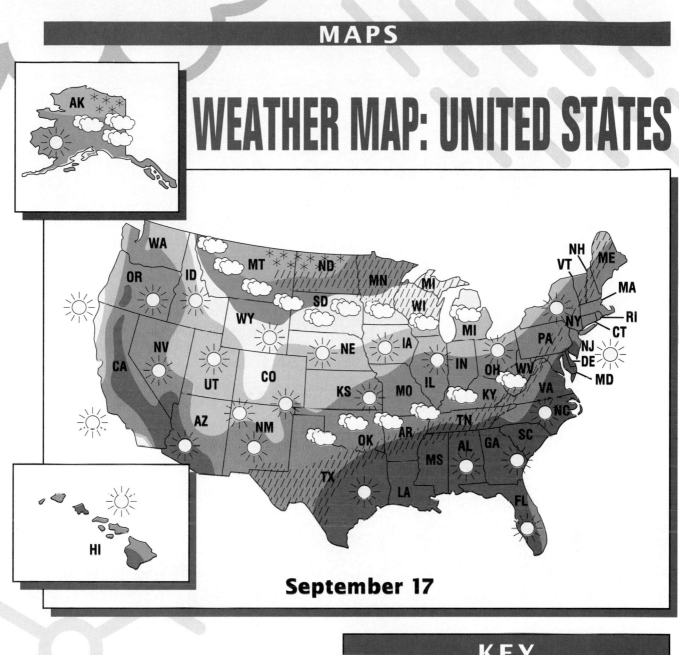

**September 17**

## KEY

| | |
|---|---|
| Very Hot | ✳✳✳✳ Snow |
| Hot | ////// Rain |
| Warm | |
| Mild | ☁ Cloudy |
| Cool | ☼ Sunny |
| Cold | |

T his glossary can help you to pronounce and find out the meanings of words in this book that you may not know.

The words are listed in alphabetical order. Guide words at the top of each page tell you the first and last words on the page.

Each word is divided into syllables. The way to pronounce each word is given next. You will be able to understand the pronunciation respelling by using the key to the right. A shorter key appears at the bottom right corner of every other page.

When a word has more than one syllable, a dark accent mark (´) shows which syllable is stressed. In some words, a light accent mark (´) shows which syllable has a less heavy stress.

Glossary entries are based on entries in *The Macmillan/McGraw-Hill School Dictionary 1.*

**Say**

| | | | |
|---|---|---|---|
| **a** | at, bad | **d** | dear, soda, bad |
| **ā** | ape, pain, day, break | **f** | five, defend, leaf, off, cough, elephant |
| **ä** | father, car, heart | | |
| **âr** | care, pair, bear, their, where | **g** | game, ago, fog, egg |
| **e** | end, pet, said, heaven, friend | **h** | hat, ahead |
| **ē** | equal, me, feet, team, piece, key | **hw** | white, whether, which |
| **i** | it, big, English, hymn | **j** | joke, enjoy, gem, page, edge |
| **ī** | ice, fine, lie, my | **k** | kite, bakery, seek, tack, cat |
| **îr** | ear, deer, here, pierce | **l** | lid, sailor, feel, ball, allow |
| **o** | odd, hot, watch | **m** | man, family, dream |
| **ō** | old, oat, toe, low | **n** | not, final, pan, knife |
| **ô** | coffee, all, taught, law, fought | **ng** | long, singer, pink |
| **ôr** | order, fork, horse, story, pour | **p** | pail, repair, soap, happy |
| **oi** | oil, toy | **r** | ride, parent, wear, more, marry |
| **ou** | out, now | **s** | sit, aside, pets, cent, pass |
| **u** | up, mud, love, double | **sh** | shoe, washer, fish, mission, nation |
| **ū** | use, mule, cue, feud, few | **t** | tag, pretend, fat, button, dressed |
| **ü** | rule, true, food | **th** | thin, panther, both |
| **u̇** | put, wood, should | **th** | this, mother, smooth |
| **ûr** | burn, hurry, term, bird, word, courage | **v** | very, favor, wave |
| | | **w** | wet, weather, reward |
| **ə** | about, taken, pencil, lemon, circus | **y** | yes, onion |
| **b** | bat, above, job | **z** | zoo, lazy, jazz, rose, dogs, houses |
| **ch** | chin, such, match | **zh** | vision, treasure, seizure |

**abandon** To leave without intending to return. The sailors *abandoned* the sinking ship.
a•ban•don (ə ban´dən) *verb*, **abandoned, abandoning.**

**absorb** To soak up or take in. A towel *absorbs* spilled water.
ab•sorb (ab sôrb´ *or* ab zôrb´) *verb*, **absorbed, absorbing.**

**alarm** A sudden fear of danger. The loud thunder filled the child with *alarm*.
a•larm (ə lärm´) *noun.*

**altar** A table or a raised place that is used for religious services.
▲ Another word that sounds like this is **alter.**
al•tar (ôl´tər) *noun.*

**aluminum** A light, soft, silver-white metal. Aluminum is the most abundant metal in the earth's crust and has many uses.
a•lu•mi•num (ə lü´mə nəm) *noun.*

**Amazon** The longest river in South America and, by volume, the largest in the world, flowing from the Andes across Brazil into the Atlantic. Its length is about 4,000 mi. (6,436 km).
Am•a•zon (am´ə zon´) *noun.*

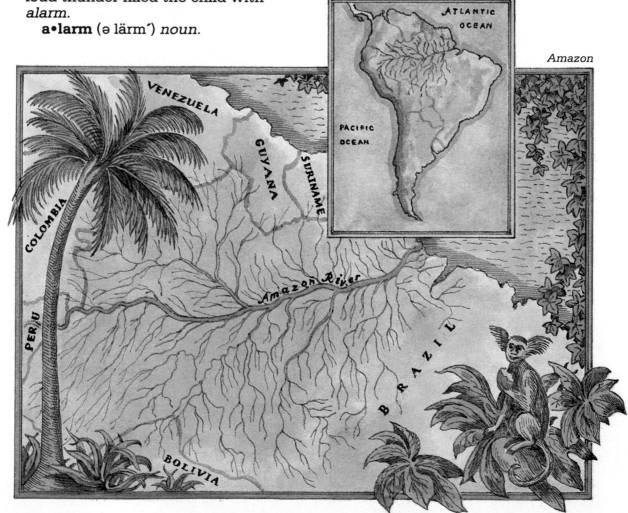

*Amazon*

**ancestor** A person from whom one is descended. Your grandparents and great-grandparents are among your *ancestors*.
   **an•ces•tor** (an´ses tər) *noun.*

*ancestor*

**anesthesia** A loss of all feeling, especially pain, that occurs when a doctor gives certain drugs to a patient. This loss of feeling may be in all or part of the body. Most patients prefer *anesthesia* to pain even during minor operations.
   **an•es•the•sia** (an´əs thē´zhə) *noun.*

**arrangement** 1. A plan or preparation. Our class made *arrangements* to visit the zoo. 2. The act of putting in order or position. *Arrangement* of the books took two hours. 3. Something put in order or position. They made a flower *arrangement* for the party.
   **ar•range•ment** (ə rānj´mənt) *noun.*

**asphalt** A brown or black substance found in the ground or obtained when petroleum is made pure. It is mixed with sand or gravel and is used to pave roads.
   **as•phalt** (as´fôlt) *noun.*

**bamboo** A tall plant that is related to grass. The bamboo has woody stems that are often hollow and are used to make fishing poles, canes, and furniture. *Noun.* —Made of bamboo. *Adjective.*
   **bam•boo** (bam bü´) *noun; adjective.*

---

**Word History**

The word **bamboo** comes from the Malay word *bambu* for the same plant.

---

*bamboo*

---

at; āpe; fär; câre; end; mē; it; īce; pîerce; hot; ōld; sông; fôrk; oil; out; up; ūse; rüle; půll; tûrn; **ch**in; si**ng**; **sh**op; **th**in; **th**is; **hw** in **wh**ite; **zh** in trea**s**ure. The symbol ə stands for the unstressed vowel sound in **a**bout, tak**e**n, penc**i**l, lem**o**n, and circ**u**s.

---

303

**band¹** To gather together in a group. The neighbors *banded* together to clean up litter in the vacant lot.
    **band** (band) *verb,* **banded, banding.**

**band²** To put a strip of cloth or other material on. Scientists *banded* the leg of the pigeon so that they could later identify it.
    **band** (band) *verb,* **banded, banding.**

**banzai** A Japanese battle cry, cheer, or greeting. This word comes from the Japanese exclamation *banzai!,* meaning "May you live ten thousand years!"
    **ban•zai** (bän´zī´) *interjection.*

**Bapa Raja** (bä´pə rä´jə)

**barrel** To move rapidly. The skater *barreled* across the ice as fast as she could go.
    **bar•rel** (bar´əl) *verb,* **barreled, barreling;** *also, British,* **barrelled, barrelling.**

**barrio** **1.** A neighborhood of a city in Spanish-speaking countries.
**2.** In a city of the United States, a neighborhood where Spanish is the main language that is spoken.
    **bar•ri•o** (bär´ē ō *or* bar´ē ō) *noun.*

**bawl** To cry or shout loudly. The child *bawled* after falling on the sidewalk. ▲ Another word that sounds like this is **ball.**
    **bawl** (bôl) *verb,* **bawled, bawling.**

**beady** Small, round, and glittering. The bird had *beady* eyes.
    **bead•y** (bē´dē) *adjective.*

**bean curd** Another word for **tofu.** A soft, white food made from mashed soybeans formed into a cake. Bean curd is used especially in Asian and vegetarian cooking.
    **bean curd** (bēn kûrd) *noun.*

**befit** To be suitable or appropriate for. The prince is treated with the dignity that *befits* his title.
    **be•fit** (bi fit´) *verb,* **befitted, befitting.**

**behaviour** *British.* Another spelling of **behavior.** A way of doing things or acting. The children's *behaviour* was good.
    **be•hav•iour** (bi hāv´yər) *noun.*

**belated** Late. I received a *belated* birthday present a week after my birthday.
    **be•la•ted** (bi lā´tid) *adjective.*

*barrio*

**biologist** A person who studies the science of living things.
> **bi•ol•o•gist** (bī ol′ə jist) *noun.*

**bird of paradise** A songbird of Australia, New Guinea, and neighboring islands. The male of the species is noted for its brilliant feathers.
> **bird of par•a•dise** (bûrd əv par′ə dīs′) *noun.*

*boa constrictor*

**browse** To feed or nibble on the leaves or twigs of a tree or shrub. The giraffe *browsed* on the tree.
> **browse** (brouz) *verb,* **browsed, browsing.**

*browse*

**boa constrictor** A large snake that is found in Mexico and in Central and South America. A boa constrictor is not poisonous. It kills its prey by winding around it and squeezing it to death.
> **bo•a con•stric•tor** (bō′ə kən strik′tər) *noun.*

**border** To lie on the edge of. California *borders* Oregon.
> **bor•der** (bôr′dər) *verb,* **bordered, bordering.**

**bough** A large branch of a tree. We fastened the swing to a *bough* of the tree. ▲ Another word that sounds like this is **bow** (*verb*).
> **bough** (bou) *noun.*

**brandish** To wave, shake, or swing in an angry or threatening way. He *brandished* his cane at the truck that splashed him.
> **bran•dish** (bran′dish) *verb,* **brandished, brandishing.**

---

at; āpe; fär; câre; end; mē; it; īce; pîerce; hot; ōld; sông; fôrk; oil; out; up; ūse; rüle; pùll; tûrn; chin; sing; shop; thin; **th**is; hw in white; zh in treasure. The symbol ə stands for the unstressed vowel sound in about, taken, pencil, lemon, and circus.

305

**Buddhist** Relating to Buddhism, a religion that is based on the teachings of Buddha, an Indian religious leader who lived from about 563 B.C. to about 483 B.C.
  **Bud•dhist** (bùd´ist *or* bü´dist) *adjective.*

# C

**Camila** (kä mē´lä)

**Caracas** The capital and largest city of Venezuela, in the northern part of the country.
  **Ca•rac•as** (kə rä´ kəs) *noun.*

**Carlitos** (kär lē´tōs)

**cavern** A large cave.
  **cav•ern** (kav´ərn) *noun.*

*cavern*

**character** 1. All the things that make a person or object different from others. The countryside has a different *character* as you travel west. 2. Strength of mind, courage, and honesty. Political leaders should be persons of great *character*. 3. A person in a book, play, story, or movie. Who is your favorite *character* in that book?
  **char•ac•ter** (kar´ik tər) *noun.*

**Cheo** (chā´ō)

**Chewandswallow** (chü´ənd swol´ō)

**citizen** A person who was born in a country or who chooses to live in and become a member of a country. When you are a citizen of the United States, you have certain rights, such as the right to vote for people who hold government office. You also have responsibilities, such as serving on a jury.
  **cit•i•zen** (sit´ə zən) *noun.*

**clover** A small plant that has leaves made up of three parts and rounded, fragrant flower heads of white, red, or purple flowers.
  **clo•ver** (klō´vər) *noun.*

**coax** To persuade or influence by soft-spoken words or pleasing actions. I tried to *coax* my parents into letting me go to camp next summer by promising to work hard in school.
  **coax** (kōks) *verb,* **coaxed, coaxing.**

**cockatoo** A parrot that has white feathers and a large comb, or crest, on its head. Cockatoos live in Australia and Asia.
  **cock•a•too** (kok´ə tü) *noun.*

*cockatoo*

**cock-of-the-rock**  A bird from South America. The male bird is mostly orange and has a large comb, or crest, on its head.
**cock-of-the-rock** (kok´əv <u>th</u>ə rok´) *noun.*

**commotion**  A noisy confusion; disorder. There was a *commotion* during the game as the crowd booed the referee's decision.
**com•mo•tion** (kə mō´shən) *noun.*

**community**  **1.** A group of different plants and animals that live together in the same area and depend on one another for their survival.  **2.** A group of people who live together in the same place. Our *community* voted to build a new library.
**com•mu•ni•ty** (kə mū´ni tē) *noun,* *plural* **communities.**

*conservatory*

*community*

**complicated**  Hard to understand or do. The directions for putting together the bicycle were too *complicated* for me to follow.
**com•pli•cat•ed** (kom´pli kā´tid) *adjective.*

**conservatory**  A greenhouse, or special building with glass walls and a glass roof, for growing and displaying plants. Hundreds of orchids were growing under the glass roof of the *conservatory.*
**con•serv•a•to•ry** (kən sûr´və tôr´ē) *noun, plural* **conservatories.**

**convert**  To change into something different. The new owner *converted* the large house into an inn.
**con•vert** (kən vûrt´) *verb,* **converted, converting.**

**cooperate**  To work together. The three classes *cooperate* in planning a picnic at the end of the school year.
**co•op•er•ate** (kō op´ə rāt´) *verb,* **cooperated, cooperating.**

---

**Word History**

The word **cooperate** comes from *co-,* a Latin word beginning that means "together," and the Latin word *operari,* meaning "to work."

---

at; āpe; fär; câre; end; mē; it; īce; pîerce; hot; ōld; sông; fôrk; oil; out; up; ūse; rüle; pùll; tûrn; **ch**in; si**ng**; **sh**op; **th**in; <u>**th**</u>is; **hw** in **wh**ite; **zh** in trea**s**ure. The symbol ə stands for the unstressed vowel sound in about, taken, pencil, lemon, and circus.

*coral*

**defend** **1.** To speak or act in support of. The group expressed an opinion and *defended* it with facts and arguments. **2.** To guard against attack or danger; protect. A goalie's job is to *defend* the goal against the other team.
    **de•fend** (di fend´) *verb*, **defended, defending.**

**dejected** Sad or depressed. The basketball team felt *dejected* after losing the game.
    **de•ject•ed** (di jek´tid) *adjective.*

*dejected*

**coral** A hard substance that is like stone and is found in tropical seas. Coral is made up of the skeletons of tiny sea animals. *Noun.* —Made of coral. A *coral* reef surrounds the island. *Adjective.*
    **cor•al** (kôr´əl) *noun; adjective.*

**creative** Having or showing ability to make or do something in a new way. A *creative* person did this unusual painting.
    **cre•a•tive** (krē ā´tiv) *adjective.*

308

**detect** To find out; discover. Call the fire department if you *detect* smoke.
**de•tect** (di tekt´) *verb,* **detected, detecting.**

**dignity** The condition of being aware of one's honor and worthiness, as shown in a proud, calm appearance or manner. Despite great hardship and poverty, my grandparents kept their *dignity.*
**dig•ni•ty** (dig´ni tē) *noun.*

**disposable** Made to be thrown away after being used. We used *disposable* paper plates at the picnic.
**dis•pos•a•ble** (di spō´zə bəl) *adjective.*

**doko** Japanese for "where."
**do•ko** (dō kō).

**downspout** A pipe that carries rain water from the roof down toward the ground.
**down•spout** (doun´spout´) *noun.*

**drought** A long period of time when there is very little rain or no rain at all. The farmer's crops dried up during the *drought.*
**drought** (drout) *noun.*

**Earth-positive** Good for Earth or the environment. The committee was formed to support *Earth-positive* causes.
**Earth-pos•i•tive** (ûrth´poz´i tiv) *adjective.*

**editor** **1.** A person in charge of a newspaper or magazine or one of its sections. The newspaper *editor* wrote an article in favor of raising city taxes. **2.** A person who corrects and checks something written so that it is ready to be printed. The *editor* made changes in the book after talking with the author.
**ed•i•tor** (ed´i tər) *noun.*

**election** The act of choosing by voting. There is an *election* for the President every four years in the United States.
**e•lec•tion** (i lek´shən) *noun.*

*election*

at; āpe; fär; câre; end; mē; it; īce; pîerce; hot; ōld; sông; fôrk; oil; out; up; ūse; rüle; pu̇ll; tûrn; **ch**in; si**ng**; **sh**op; **th**in; **th**is; **hw** in **wh**ite; **zh** in trea**s**ure. The symbol **ə** stands for the unstressed vowel sound in **a**bout, tak**e**n, penc**i**l, lem**o**n, and circ**u**s.

**endangered** Threatened with
becoming extinct; dying out. Laws
protect *endangered* animals.
  **en•dan•gered** (en dān´jərd)
  *adjective.*

*endangered*

**engineer** A person who is trained
in using scientific knowledge for
practical things. An engineer may
plan and design bridges, roads, or
airplanes.
  **en•gi•neer** (en´jə nîr´) *noun.*

**enthusiastic** Having a strong feeling
of excitement and interest about
something. We were all *enthusiastic*
about going on a picnic.
  **en•thu•si•as•tic** (en thü zē as´tik)
  *adjective.*

**environment** The air, the water, the
soil, and all the other things that
surround a person, animal, or plant.
The environment can affect the
growth and health of living things.
The people who run the zoo try to
make each animal's surroundings like
its natural *environment.*
  **en•vi•ron•ment** (en vī´rən mənt *or*
  en vī´ərn mənt) *noun.*

**Exxon Valdez** (ek´son val dēz´ *or*
väl dez´)

**feature** **1.** A story of special interest in a newspaper or magazine. The reporter wrote a *feature* about the new mayor of the city. **2.** A part or quality of something. An important *feature* of the camel is its ability to go for days without water.
**fea•ture** (fē′chər) *noun.*

**fine¹** Of very high quality; very good; excellent. The pianist is a *fine* musician.
**fine** (fīn) *adjective.*

**fine²** To punish someone by making him or her pay an amount of money. The judge *fined* the driver for going through a red light.
**fine** (fīn) *verb,* **fined, fining.**

**fluid** A liquid. The doctor told me to drink plenty of *fluids*.
**flu•id** (flü′id) *noun.*

**forecast** A statement that tells what will or may happen; prediction. Let's listen to the weather *forecast* to find out if it's going to rain today.
**fore•cast** (fôr′kast′) *noun.*

**fragrant** Having a sweet or pleasing smell. The flowers made the whole room *fragrant*.
**fra•grant** (frā′grənt) *adjective.*

**froth** A mass of bubbles formed in or on a liquid; foam. A fine *froth* appeared as we slowly boiled the milk.
**froth** (frôth) *noun.*

**fungi** *Also,* **funji.** A dish of African origin made with cornmeal.
**fun•gi** (fun′jē) *noun.*

**funnel** A kitchen tool that has a wide cone at one end and a thin tube at the other. You can use a funnel to pour something into a container that has a small opening.
**fun•nel** (fun′əl) *noun.*

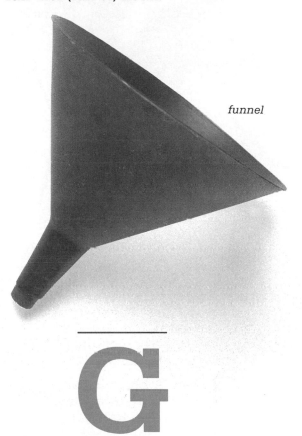

*funnel*

**G**

**generation** **1.** One step in the line of descent from a common relative. A grandparent, parent, and child make up three *generations*. **2.** A group of persons born around the same time. My parents call me and my friends the younger *generation*.
**gen•er•a•tion** (jen′ə rā′shən) *noun.*

at; āpe; fär; câre; end; mē; it; īce; pîerce; hot; ōld; sông; fôrk; oil; out; up; ūse; rüle; pu̇ll; tûrn; chin; sing; shop; thin; **th**is; hw in **wh**ite; zh in treasure. The symbol ə stands for the unstressed vowel sound in about, taken, pencil, lemon, and circus.

311

*gnat*

**hail¹** To greet or attract the attention of by calling or shouting. I *hailed* my friends across the street by calling to them.
   **hail** (hāl) *verb,* **hailed, hailing.**

**hail²** Small, round pieces of ice that fall in a shower like rain. The *hail* came down so hard that it crushed many of the flowers in the garden.
   **hail** (hāl) *noun.*

**herd** A group of animals that live or travel together. A *herd* of cattle grazed in the pasture. ▲ Another word that sounds like this is **heard.**
   **herd** (hûrd) *noun.*

**gnat** Any of various small, winged insects that have sharp, piercing mouth parts. Some gnats suck blood, but others feed on plants.
   **gnat** (nat) *noun.*

**Gorgonzola** A blue cheese of Italian origin that has a strong smell.
   **Gor•gon•zo•la** (gôr´gən zō´lə) *noun.*

**gradual** Happening little by little; moving or changing slowly. We watched the *gradual* growth of the seeds into plants in our vegetable garden.
   **grad•u•al** (graj´ü əl) *adjective.*

**great-aunt** An aunt of one's father or mother.
   **great-aunt** (grāt´ant´ *or* grāt´änt´) *noun.*

**grief** 1. Trouble; annoyance. You have caused enough *grief* for one day.
2. A very great feeling of being sad. My *grief* at the death of my dog was something I'll never forget.
   **grief** (grēf) *noun.*

*herd*

**hesitate** To wait or stop a moment, especially because of feeling unsure. The speaker *hesitated* and looked down at his notes.
   **hes•i•tate** (hez´i tāt´) *verb,* **hesitated, hesitating.**

**hoarse** Having a deep, rough, or harsh sound. The teacher's voice was *hoarse* from a bad cold. ▲ Another word that sounds like this is **horse.**
   **hoarse** (hôrs) *adjective.*

**interlocking** Fitting together closely. None of the *interlocking* parts of this machine can move without causing the other parts to move as well.
   **in•ter•lock•ing** (in´tər lok´ing) *adjective.*

*interlocking*

I

**incense** A substance that has a pleasing smell when it is burned. After the *incense* was lighted, it created a spicy smell in the room.
   **in•cense** (in´sens´) *noun.*

**incident** Something that happens; event. My neighbors told us about a funny *incident* on their trip to Florida.
   **in•ci•dent** (in´si dənt) *noun.*

**insulating** Having a covering or surrounding of material that slows or stops the flow of electricity, heat, or sound. Putting up *insulating* storm windows allows us to stay warm inside in winter.
   **in•su•lat•ing** (in´sə lā´ting) *adjective.*

**isle** An island. Isles are usually small islands. ▲ Other words that sound like this are **aisle** and **I'll.**
   **isle** (īl) *noun.*

**intensive care** Careful and complete medical attention. The patient needed *intensive care* while he was in the hospital.
   **in•ten•sive care** (in ten´siv kâr) *noun.*

at; āpe; fär; câre; end; mē; it; īce; pîerce; hot; ōld; sông; fôrk; oil; out; up; ūse; rüle; pùll; tûrn; chin; sing; shop; thin; <u>th</u>is; hw in white; zh in treasure. The symbol ə stands for the unstressed vowel sound in about, taken, pencil, lemon, and circus.

*jaguar*

# J

**jaguar** A large animal that belongs to the cat family. The short fur of a jaguar is golden and is marked with black rings with spots in their centers. Jaguars are found in Mexico, Central America, and South America.
**jag•uar** (jag´wär) *noun.*

---

**Word History**

The word **jaguar** comes from the Spanish word *yaguar* and the Portuguese word *jaguar,* which in turn came from the languages of the Guarani and Tupi Native Americans of the Amazon region.

---

**jasmine** A fragrant bell-shaped flower that grows in yellow, white, or pink clusters.
**jas•mine** (jaz´min) *noun.*

# K

**Kapiti Plain** (kə pē´tē plān)

**kapok tree** A tropical tree that produces a light, fluffy fiber used as a stuffing for life preservers, pillows, and mattresses.
**ka•pok tree** (kā´pok trē) *noun.*

314

**kimono** A loose robe that is tied with a sash. Kimonos are worn by both men and women in Japan, usually on holidays or other special occasions.
**ki•mo•no** (ki mō′nə) *noun.*

**kinship** **1.** Any relationship or close connection. The children who had gone to camp together felt a great *kinship.* **2.** A family relationship.
**kin•ship** (kin′ship′) *noun.*

**Ki-pat** (kē pat′)

**Kitamura** (kē tä mü rä)

**Leonardo da Vinci** 1452–1519, Italian artist and scientist. One of his most famous paintings is the *Mona Lisa.*
**Le•o•nar•do da Vin•ci** (lē′ə när′dō də vin′chē) *noun.*

*Leonardo da Vinci*

**liberty** The ability to act, speak, or think the way one pleases. The people lost their *liberty* under the dictator's rule.
**lib•er•ty** (lib′ər tē) *noun.*

**lull** To make or become calm. The sound of rain on the roof *lulled* the baby to sleep. The storm finally *lulled.*
**lull** (lul) *verb,* **lulled, lulling.**

**lupine** A plant related to the pea that bears spikes of white, yellow, blue, or purple flowers.
**lu•pine** (lü′pin) *noun.*

*lupine*

at; āpe; fär; câre; end; mē; it; īce; pîerce; hot; ōld; sông; fôrk; oil; out; up; ūse; rüle; pull; tûrn; chin; sing; shop; thin; this; hw in white; zh in treasure. The symbol ə stands for the unstressed vowel sound in about, taken, pencil, lemon, and circus.

**macaw** Any of several long-tailed, brilliantly colored parrots of Central and South America. The macaw has a large, strong beak, with which it cracks nuts. It is the largest parrot.
**ma•caw** (mə kô´) *noun.*

**maiden** A girl or young woman who is not married.
**maid•en** (mā´dən) *noun.*

**mammal** A kind of animal that is warm-blooded and has a backbone. Female mammals have glands that produce milk to feed their young. Most mammals are covered with fur or have some hair. Human beings, cattle, dogs, cats, and whales are mammals.
**mam•mal** (mam´əl) *noun.*

**mandarin** A deep orange color.
**man•da•rin** (man´dər in) *adjective.*

**mango** A yellowish-red fruit that has a sweet, spicy taste and a hard seed in the center. It grows on a tropical evergreen tree.
**man•go** (mang´gō) *noun.*

**mantel** The shelf above a fireplace. This is also called a **mantelpiece**.
**man•tel** (man´təl) *noun.*

**marine** Having to do with or living in the sea. Whales àre *marine* animals.
**ma•rine** (mə rēn´) *adjective.*

**migrate** To move from one place to another. Many birds *migrate* to the south in the fall.
**mi•grate** (mī´grāt) *verb,* **migrated, migrating.**

**mimic** To imitate. The comedian could *mimic* the voices of famous people.
**mim•ic** (mim´ik) *verb,* **mimicked, mimicking.**

**Miyo** (mē yō)

**mother-of-pearl** Made of a hard, rainbow-colored layer lining the shells of pearl oysters and certain other animals with hard outer shells. This material is used in making buttons and jewelry.
**moth•er-of-pearl** (mu<u>th</u>´ər əv pûrl´) *adjective.*

*mango*

**municipal** Having to do with the government and day-to-day business of a city or town. We are having a *municipal* election this week to elect a new town sheriff.
　**mu•nic•i•pal** (mū nis´ə pəl) *adjective.*

**mural** A picture painted on a wall or ceiling. A mural usually covers most of the wall. The students' *mural* showed events from state history.
　**mu•ral** (myúr´əl) *noun.*

**oil spill** An accidental dumping of oil into a river or ocean, usually from an oil tanker or a place where oil is processed. An *oil spill* is very dangerous to sea life.
　**oil spill** (oil spil) *noun.*

*mural*

**necessity** Something that cannot be done without; requirement. Food, clothing, and shelter are the *necessities* of life.
　**ne•ces•si•ty** (ni ses´i tē) *noun,* *plural* **necessities.**

**overcome** To get over or deal with. You must *overcome* your fear of water before you can learn how to swim.
　**o•ver•come** (ō´vər kum´) *verb,* **overcame, overcoming.**

at; āpe; fär; câre; end; mē; it; īce; pîerce; hot; ōld; sông; fôrk; oil; out; up; ūse; rüle; púll; tûrn; **ch**in; si**ng**; **sh**op; **th**in; **th**is; **hw** in **wh**ite; **zh** in treasure. The symbol ə stands for the unstressed vowel sound in about, taken, pencil, lemon, and circus.

**passionately** In a way that shows very strong feelings. The mayor spoke *passionately* today about the need for a new high school.
**pas•sion•ate•ly** (pash´ə nit lē) *adverb.*

**pawpaw** *Also,* **papaw.** A fruit that has yellow flesh and a bananalike taste. Pawpaw trees grow mainly in the central United States.
**paw•paw** (pô´pô) *noun.*

*permanent*

**permanent** A wavy or curly hairdo that lasts several months, set in the hair with a chemical solution or with heat. *Noun.* —Lasting or meant to last; enduring. After graduating from college, I started looking for a *permanent* job. *Adjective.*
**per•ma•nent** (pûr´mə nənt) *noun; adjective.*

**pierce** 1. To make a hole through. A nail *pierced* the tire of my bicycle. 2. To pass through; penetrate. A shrill cry *pierced* the stillness of the night.
**pierce** (pîrs) *verb,* **pierced, piercing.**

**plantain** A kind of banana. Plantains contain a good deal of starch. They are cooked before being eaten.
**plan•tain** (plan´tən) *noun.*

*plantain*

**politician** A person who holds or seeks government office.
**pol•i•ti•cian** (pol´i tish´ən) *noun.*

**pollen** A yellowish powder made by flowers. Pollen is made up of the male cells of flowering plants. It fertilizes the female cells so that they can form seeds.
**pol•len** (pol´ən) *noun.*

**pollinate** To carry pollen from one flower to another, or from one part to another part of the same flower, so that the plant can form seeds.
**pol•li•nate** (pol´ə nāt´) *verb,* **pollinated, pollinating.**

**portrait** A picture of someone or something. The artist painted a *portrait* of the new mayor.
**por•trait** (pôr´trit *or* pôr´trāt) *noun.*

**precious metal** A metal that has great value. Gold is a precious metal.
**pre•cious met•al** (presh´əs met´əl) *noun.*

*prehistoric*

**prehistoric** Belonging to a time before people started writing history. Dinosaurs were *prehistoric* animals.
**pre•his•tor•ic** (prē´his tôr´ik) *adjective.*

**Preserven el parque Elysian** Spanish for "Save Elysian Park."
**Pre•ser•ven el par•que E•ly•sian** (prā ser´ben el pär´kā ā lē´syän).

**prey 1.** The habit of hunting animals for food. A tiger is a beast of *prey*. **2.** An animal that is hunted by another animal for food. Rabbits, birds, and snakes are the *prey* of foxes. ▲ Another word that sounds like this is **pray.**
**prey** (prā) *noun.*

**proverb** A short saying that expresses an idea that many people believe to be true. "Haste makes waste" is a proverb.
**prov•erb** (prov´ərb) *noun.*

**prow** The front part of a boat or ship; bow.
**prow** (prou) *noun.*

**quantity** A number or amount. That restaurant buys large *quantities* of food.
**quan•ti•ty** (kwon´ti tē) *noun, plural* **quantities.**

---

### Word History

The word **quantity** comes from the French word *quantité*, which in turn came from the Latin word *quantus*, meaning "how much" or "how large."

---

at; āpe; fär; câre; end; mē; it; īce; pîerce; hot; ōld; sông; fôrk; oil; out; up; ūse; rüle; pu̇ll; tûrn; chin; sing; shop; thin; this; hw in white; zh in treasure. The symbol ə stands for the unstressed vowel sound in about, taken, pencil, lemon, and circus.

**radar** A device that uses radio waves to find and track objects, such as airplanes and automobiles.
**ra•dar** (rā´där) *noun*.

*recycle*

**recycle** To make fit to be used again. Most cities in our state *recycle* cans and bottles.
**re•cy•cle** (rē sī´ kəl) verb, **recycled, recycling.**

**reef** A ridge of sand, rock, or coral that lies at or near the surface of the ocean or another body of water.
**reef** (rēf) *noun*.

**retire** To stop working completely or at a particular job. My parents are thinking of *retiring* when they are sixty-five.
**re•tire** (ri tīr´) *verb*, **retired, retiring.**

**rhythm** A regular or orderly repeating of sounds or movements. We marched to the *rhythm* of a steady drumbeat.
**rhythm** (ri<u>th</u>´əm) *noun*.

**rouse** To awaken from sleep or rest. The loud noise *roused* us.
**rouse** (rouz) *verb*, **roused, rousing.**

**ruins** The remains of something destroyed or decayed. They found the *ruins* of an old stone wall.
**ru•ins** (rü´inz) *plural noun*.

**Rumphius** (rum´fē əs)

**salmon** A large fish with a silver-colored body. Most salmon live in salt water but swim to fresh water to lay their eggs.
**sal•mon** (sam´ən) *noun*.

*salmon*

**San José** (san hō zā´)

**sand** To scrape and smooth with sandpaper or sand. They *sanded* the walls before they painted them.
    **sand** (sand) *verb*, **sanded, sanding.**

**satellite** A spacecraft that moves in an orbit around the earth, the moon, or other bodies in space. Satellites are used to forecast the weather; to connect radio, telephone, and television communications; and to provide information about conditions in space.
    **sat•el•lite** (sat´ə līt´) *noun.*

**scowl** To frown in an angry way. The father *scowled* at his child's rude behavior.
    **scowl** (skoul) *verb*, **scowled, scowling.**

**scroll** A roll of paper or other material with writing or drawing on it. Each end of a scroll is often rolled around a rod.
    **scroll** (skrōl) *noun.*

**seek** **1.** To try. Every candidate in the election will *seek* to win. **2.** To try to find; go in search of. My family was *seeking* our missing pet.
    **seek** (sēk) *verb*, **sought, seeking.**

**Senhor** Sir; mister. The Portuguese form of polite address for a man. The Portuguese language is spoken in Portugal, Brazil, and other countries.
    **Se•nhor** (sin yôr´) *noun.*

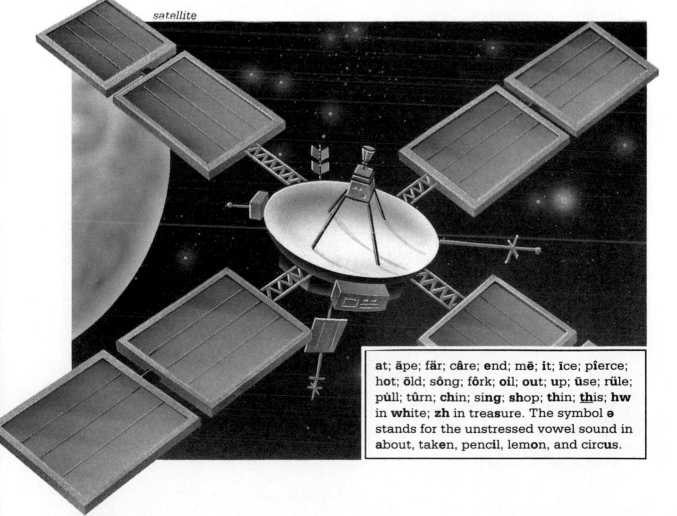
*satellite*

at; āpe; fär; câre; **e**nd; mē; it; īce; pîerce; hot; ōld; sông; fôrk; oil; out; up; ūse; rüle; p**u**ll; tûrn; **ch**in; si**ng**; **sh**op; **th**in; **th**is; **hw** in **wh**ite; **zh** in treasure. The symbol ə stands for the unstressed vowel sound in **a**bout, tak**e**n, penc**i**l, lem**o**n, and circ**u**s.

**sewer** A pipe or channel under the ground for carrying off waste.
**sew•er** (sü´ər) *noun.*

**slicker** A raincoat made of plastic or a similar waterproof material.
**slick•er** (slik´ər) *noun.*

*slicker*

**sloth** A slow-moving animal that lives in the forests of South America. Sloths use their long arms and legs and their curved claws to hang upside down from trees.
**sloth** (slôth *or* slōth) *noun.*

**soar** To fly high in the air. The bird *soared* in the sky. ▲ Another word that sounds like this is **sore.**
**soar** (sôr) *verb,* **soared, soaring.**

**solution** 1. A mixture formed by something dissolved in a liquid. Salt in water forms a *solution.* 2. The answer to a problem. We tried to find the *solution* to the puzzle.
**so•lu•tion** (sə lü´shən) *noun.*

**sought** Past tense of **seek.** Look up **seek** for more information.
**sought** (sôt) *verb.*

**sow¹** To scatter seeds over the ground; plant. The farmer will *sow* oats in this field. ▲ Other words that sound like this are **sew** and **so.**
**sow** (sō) *verb,* **sowed, sowing.**

**sow²** An adult female pig.
**sow** (sou) *noun.*

**spent** Worn-out; tired; exhausted. After the race, the *spent* runner sat down in the grass.
**spent** (spent) *adjective.*

**stress** Physical, mental, or emotional strain or pressure. She became ill because of the *stress* caused by her job.
**stress** (stres) *noun.*

**summit** The highest point. Arturo climbed to the *summit* of the mountain.
**sum•mit** (sum´it) *noun.*

*summit*

**survival** The act of staying alive. The *survival* of all the bus passengers in the accident seemed a miracle.
**sur•viv•al** (sər vī´vəl) *noun.*

**suspend** To attach so as to hang down. The swing was *suspended* from a branch.
**sus•pend** (sə spend´) *verb,* **suspended, suspending.**

---

### Word History

The word **suspend** comes from the Latin word *suspendere,* which is made up of *sus-,* a Latin word beginning that means "up," and the Latin word *pendere,* meaning "to cause to hang."

---

**take on** To deal or struggle with. No one wants to *take on* the neighborhood bully.
**take on** (tāk on) *verb,* **took on, taking on.**

**Tami** (tä mē)

**tanker** A ship, truck, or airplane that has tanks for carrying oil or another liquid.
**tank•er** (tang´kər) *noun.*

**temple¹** A building that is used for the worship of a god or gods. Long ago, the Romans built this *temple* as a place to pray to their gods.
**tem•ple** (tem´pəl) *noun.*

**temple²** The flattened part on either side of the forehead. The temple is above the cheek and in front of the ear.
**tem•ple** (tem´pəl) *noun.*

**temporary** Lasting or used for a short time only. Some students try to find *temporary* jobs for the summer.
**tem•po•rar•y** (tem´pə rer´ē) *adjective.*

**thong** A narrow strip of leather or other material that is used for attaching things. The rider tied the bag of supplies to her saddle with a *thong.*
**thong** (thông *or* thong) *noun.*

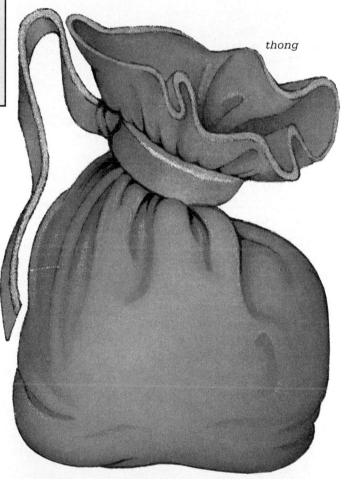

*thong*

at; āpe; fär; câre; end; mē; it; īce; pîerce; hot; ōld; sông; fôrk; oil; out; up; ūse; rüle; půll; tûrn; chin; sing; shop; thin; **th**is; hw in white; zh in treasure. The symbol ə stands for the unstressed vowel sound in about, taken, pencil, lemon, and circus.

**toucan** A bird that has a heavy body, a very large beak, and colorful feathers. Toucans are found in tropical areas of Central and South America.
  **tou•can** (tü´kan) *noun*.

*toucan*

**touch off** To cause to happen. The loud, sudden noise *touched off* the baby's crying.
  **touch off** (tuch ôf) *verb*, **touched off, touching off.**

**tropical** Having to do with or found in a region of the earth that is near the equator, or the imaginary line around the middle of the earth. Tropical areas are almost always warm. Most monkeys live in *tropical* forests.
  **trop•i•cal** (trop´i kəl) *adjective*.

**underbrush** Bushes and other plants growing under big trees in a forest or woods.
  **un•der•brush** (un´dər brush´) *noun*.

**uneventfully** Without anything important or exciting happening; in an ordinary way. After the interruption, the meeting went on *uneventfully*.
  **un•e•vent•ful•ly** (un´i vent´fə lē) *adverb*.

**vary** To become different; change. The color of the stone *varied* as we moved it around in the light.
  **vary** (vâr´ē) *verb*, **varied, varying.**

*tropical*

*Venezuela*

**Venezuela** A country in northern South America.
**Ven•e•zue•la** (ven´ə zwā´lə *or* ven´ə zwē´lə) *noun.*

**volunteer** A person who offers to help, or does something by choice, and often without pay. The teacher asked for *volunteers* for the book fair committee.
**vol•un•teer** (vol´ən tîr´) *noun.*

**waterproof** To make so that water will not pass through. My boots have been *waterproofed* with a rubber coating.
**wa•ter•proof** (wô´tər prüf´) *verb,* **waterproofed, waterproofing.**

**wetsuit** A close-fitting, one-piece garment worn for warmth while swimming, skin-diving, or surfing.
**wetsuit** (wet´süt´) *noun.*

**wharf** A landing place for boats and ships that is built along a shore; dock.
**wharf** (hwôrf *or* wôrf) *noun, plural* **wharves.**

at; āpe; fär; câre; end; mē; it; īce; pîerce; hot; ōld; sông; fôrk; oil; out; up; ūse; rüle; p* *ull; tûrn; chin; sing; shop; thin; this; hw in white; zh in treasure. The symbol ə stands for the unstressed vowel sound in about, taken, pencil, lemon, and circus.

**whisk**  A kitchen tool, usually made of wire, used especially for whipping cream or eggs.
  **whisk** (hwisk *or* wisk) *noun.*

*whisk*

**wither**  To dry up and become wrinkled. Put the cut flowers in water before they *wither*.
  **with•er** (wi<u>th</u>´er) *verb,* **withered, withering.**

**Yanomamo**  A tribe of people who live in the rain forest of Brazil.
  **Ya•no•ma•mo** (yä´nō mä´mō) *noun.*